New wave mental maths

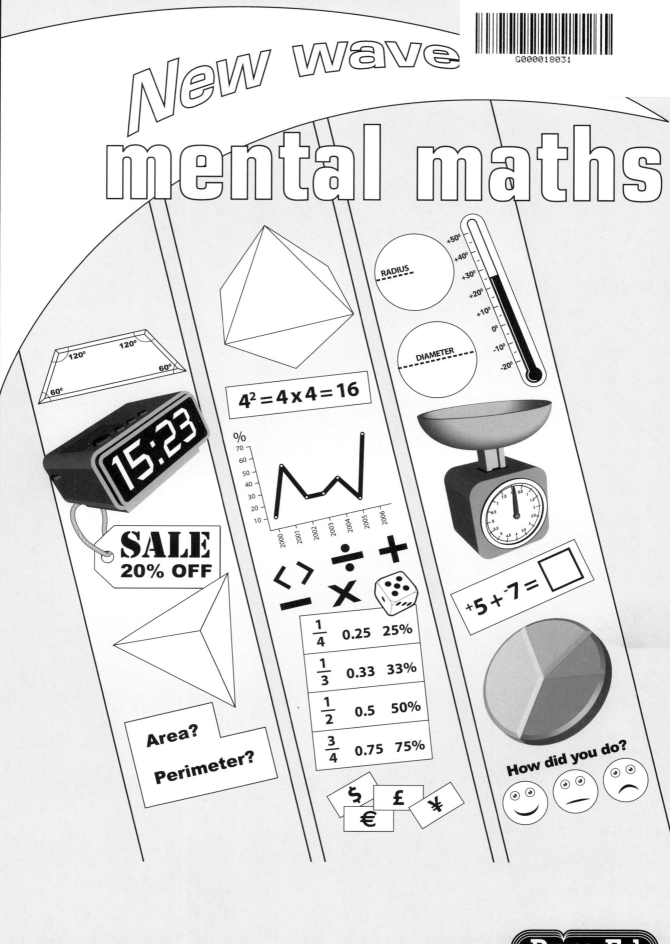

Eddy Krajcar

www.prim-ed.com

First Published in 2002 by
Prim-Ed Publishing
Revised in 2005 by Prim-Ed Publishing
Reprinted March 2007
Bosheen
New Ross
County Wexford
www.prim-ed.com

Under license to R.I.C. Publications

© Eddy Krajcar 1999

ISBN 978-1-92096-244-9

FOREWORD

New Wave Mental Maths is a series of six pupil workbooks, written to provide a comprehensive and structured daily mental maths programme. The series has been revised so that all questions cover the individual class strand and strand unit objectives required by the mathematics curriculum for Ireland.

The mental maths programme is designed to:

- *provide complete coverage of all mental maths related strands and strand units from the mathematics curriculum;*
- *encourage and develop mental calculation concepts and skills;*
- *develop and reinforce problem-solving strategies;*
- *develop and maintain speed of recall; and*
- *introduce, practice and understand a range of mathematics vocabulary.*

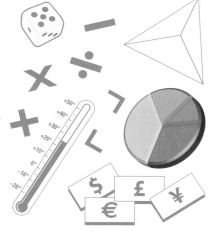

Assessment activities are provided for pupils to assess, monitor and record their own performance on a weekly basis. A separate teachers manual is available, to accompany the **New Wave Mental Maths** series. This manual contains: guidelines to help develop mental strategies; suggestions for classroom use; assessment; list of concepts developed and answers.

CONTENTS

PUPIL RECORD SHEET

Date	Week 1		Date	Week 2		Date	Week 3		Date	Week 4		Date	Week 5		Date	Week 6		Date	Week 7		Date	Week 8		Date	Week 9		Date	Week 10	
	M			M			M			M			M			M			M			M			M			M	
	Tu.			Tu.			Tu.			Tu.			Tu.			Tu.			Tu.			Tu.			Tu.			Tu.	
	W			W			W			W			W			W			W			W			W			W	
	Th.			Th.			Th.			Th.			Th.			Th.			Th.			Th.			Th.			Th.	
	F			F			F			F			F			F			F			F			F			F	

Date	Week 11		Date	Week 12		Date	Week 13		Date	Week 14		Date	Week 15		Date	Week 16		Date	Week 17		Date	Week 18		Date	Week 19		Date	Week 20	
	M			M			M			M			M			M			M			M			M			M	
	Tu.			Tu.			Tu.			Tu.			Tu.			Tu.			Tu.			Tu.			Tu.			Tu.	
	W			W			W			W			W			W			W			W			W			W	
	Th.			Th.			Th.			Th.			Th.			Th.			Th.			Th.			Th.			Th.	
	F			F			F			F			F			F			F			F			F			F	

New wave mental maths   www.prim-ed.com   Prim-Ed Publishing

PUPIL RECORD SHEET

Date		Week 21	Date	Week 22	Date	Week 23	Date	Week 24	Date	Week 25	Date	Week 26	Date	Week 27	Date	Week 28	Date	Week 29	Date	Week 30
		M		M		M		M		M		M		M		M		M		M
		Tu.		Tu.		Tu.		Tu.		Tu.		Tu.		Tu.		Tu.		Tu.		Tu.
		W		W		W		W		W		W		W		W		W		W
		Th.		Th.		Th.		Th.		Th.		Th.		Th.		Th.		Th.		Th.
		F		F		F		F		F		F		F		F		F		F

Date		Week 31	Date	Week 32	Date	Week 33	Date	Week 34	Date	Week 35	Date	Week 36	Date	Week 37	Date	Week 38	Date	Week 39	Date	Week 40
		M		M		M		M		M		M		M		M		M		M
		Tu.		Tu.		Tu.		Tu.		Tu.		Tu.		Tu.		Tu.		Tu.		Tu.
		W		W		W		W		W		W		W		W		W		W
		Th.		Th.		Th.		Th.		Th.		Th.		Th.		Th.		Th.		Th.
		F		F		F		F		F		F		F		F		F		F

MONDAY

1. Round 6.23 to one decimal place.

2. Write the prime numbers between 1 and 10.

   _____, _____, _____, and _____

3. If a clock shows 9 o'clock, what is the angle between the two hands?
   ☐ 45° ☐ 90° ☐ 9°

4. The circumference of a circle is approximately ☐ 2 ☐ 3 ☐ 4 times longer than the diameter.

5. $^4/_5 + ^4/_5 =$

6. Write one million as a numeral.

7. Circle +7 on the number line.

8. $2^2 =$

9. This is the net of a

10. What is the area of a square with 4-cm sides? _____ cm²

11. $^2/_3 \times 3 =$

12. Simplify $^5/_{10}$.

13. Name this shape.

14. Is 213 divisible by 3?

15. 10% of 100 =

16. $3\,^3/_4$ rounded = 3 or 4?

17. $(4 \times 5) - 10 =$

18. What is the 24-hour time for 6.00 p.m.?

    _____ hours

19. What is the lowest common denominator (LCD) for $^1/_2$ and $^1/_5$?
    (a) 8 ☐ (b) 10 ☐ (c) 20 ☐

20. $4 - 0.2 =$

TUESDAY

1. Round 8.06 to one decimal place.

2. The time is 2.15 p.m. in Ireland and 3.15 p.m. in Spain. What is the time difference?

3. Round $2\,^7/_{10}$ to the nearest whole number.

4. What is the radius of a circle if its diameter is 5 cm? _____ cm

5. $3^2 =$

6. $16 = (a + 8)$ so a =

7. $(5 \times 5) + (2 \times 10) =$

8. A cuboid has:

   _____ faces

   _____ edges

   _____ vertices

9. The LCD for $^1/_4$ and $^3/_{10}$ is
   (a) 10 ☐ (b) 15 ☐ (c) 20 ☐ (d) 24 ☐

10. What is the perimeter of an equilateral triangle with 7-cm sides?

    _____ cm

11. Tick the largest. ☐ $^1/_2$ ☐ $^3/_4$ ☐ $^2/_6$

12. $^1/_2 =$ _____ %

13. Place value of 8 in 82 411?

14. Name this shape.

On the circle diagram label:

15. The radius 'A'.

16. The diameter 'B'.

17. The circumference 'C'.

    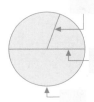

18. Write one million and one as a numeral.

19. $5\overline{)105} =$

20. $4 \times ^3/_4 =$

1. Round 4.27 to one decimal place.
2. This is the net of a

3. 4, 9, 14,
4. Write one million and ten as a numeral.

5. 6 − 0.3 =
6. Write the composite numbers between 1 and 10.

___ , ___ , ___ , ___ and ___

7. What is the 24-hour time for 9.00 p.m.?

___ hours

8. 70 = double a *so* a =

9. 2^3 = 2 x 2 x 2 =

10. (18 ÷ 3) + 8 =

11. Simplify $^6/_9$.
12. If a clock shows 3 o'clock, what is the size of the angle between the hands?
    ☐ *45°* ☐ *90°* ☐ *180°*

13. 20% of €100 = €

14. Write the numeral sixteen point seven.
15. The factors of 4 are 1, 2 and 4. ☐ *true* ☐ *false*

16. 4.1, 8.2, 16.4,

17. 9 x $^2/_3$ =
18. If a jar contains 4 chocolate chip cookies, 6 banana cookies and 10 coconut cookies, what is the probability of picking a chocolate chip cookie?

___ in ___

19. The meaning of 8 in 85 633 is

20. 6^2 =

1. Round 3.39 to one decimal place.

2. $^3/_4 + ^3/_4$ =
3. The circumference of a circle is approximately
   ☐ *2* ☐ *3* ☐ *4* times longer than the diameter.

4. 2.5 ÷ 5 = 0.
5. What is the diameter of a circle if its radius is 6 cm?

___ cm

6. A triangular prism has:

   faces

   edges

   vertices

7. (3 + 5) x (3 + 4) =

8. 3^3 = 3 x 3 x 3 =

9. Round $3^3/_7$ (nearest whole number).
10. The time is 7.12 a.m. in Ireland and 8.12 a.m. in France. What is the time difference?

11. Circle −6 on the number line.

12. 60, 600, 6 000,

13. Write the numeral thirty two point one.
14. Tick the smallest. ☐ $^4/_6$ ☐ $^8/_9$ ☐ $^1/_3$

15. $^1/_4$ = ___ %
16. The factors of 6 are:

   ___ , ___ , ___ , and ___

17. 2, 6, 12, 20, 30,
18. Write one million one hundred as a numeral.

19. 5^2 =
20. What is the 24-hour time for 4.30 a.m.?

___ hours

1. Write the numeral sixty two point five.
2. What is the radius of a circle with a 10-cm diameter?

   _____ cm
3. Name this shape.

4. Round 7.53 to one decimal place.
5. What is the place value of 9 in 962 000?

6. $90 + b = 2 \times 70$ so $b =$
7. Write one million, one hundred and one thousand as a numeral.

8. $18.5 \div 10 =$
9. If a clock shows 6 o'clock, what is the size of the angle created by the hands?

   ☐ 90° ☐ 45° ☐ 60° ☐ 180°

10. Simplify $^{10}/_{15}$.
11. Circle −5 on the number line.

12. $7 - 0.9 =$
13. This is the net of a

14. 30% of €50.00 = €

15. Is 3.7 rounded to 3 or 4?

16. $(6 \times 5) - 20 =$
17. A regular pentagon has 7-cm sides. What is its perimeter?

   _____ cm

18. $10 \times ^2/_5 =$
19. $4.04 > 4.20$ ☐ true ☐ false
20. The time is 5 p.m. in Ireland and 7 p.m. in Egypt. What is the time difference?

1. Write the numeral thirty one point eight.
2.

   Draw a 270° turn clockwise.

3. Is 715 divisible by 5?

4. $(9 \times 5) \div (30 \div 6) =$

5. 15, 30, 45, _____
6. Write the prime numbers between 11 and 20.

   _____, _____, _____, and _____

7. $2^4 = 2 \times 2 \times 2 \times 2 =$

8. $^3/_4 + ^2/_4 + ^3/_4 =$
9. Name this shape.

10. What is the radius of a circle if its diameter is 3 m?

    _____ m

11. $200 \div 5 =$

12. Simplify $^{12}/_{18}$.
13. What would be the area of an oblong field 100 m by 8 m? _____ m²
14. Name this shape.

15. $8 \times ^3/_4 =$
16. If there are £0.60 (UK) to €1.00, how many euro would you get for £3.00 (UK)?

17. $23.5 \div 10 =$
18. A cube has:

    _____ faces

    _____ edges

    _____ vertices

19. $^1/_{10} =$ _____ %

20. Round 8.6.

WEDNESDAY

1. Write the numeral twenty point seven.

2. $41.3 \div 10 =$

3. Write one million, one hundred and one as a numeral.

4. $80 + b = 60 \times 2$ *so* b =

5. If a clock shows 9 o'clock, what is the size of the angle?
   ☐ *90°* ☐ *45°* ☐ *60°*

6. $6.05 < 6.60$ ☐ *true* ☐ *false*

7. What is the radius of a circle if its diameter is 4 cm?

   cm

8. Round 5.86 to one decimal place.

9. What is the meaning of 4 in 417 200?

10. The circumference of a circle is approximately how many times longer than the diameter?

11. 40% of €80 = €

12. Tick the largest ☐ $^1/_{10}$ ☐ $^3/_5$ ☐ $^4/_{10}$

13. $9 - 0.9 =$

14. $6\overline{)126} =$

15. 25, 50,   , 100

16. $^3/_4 =$ %

17. Round 8.13. Is it 8.1 or 8.2?

18. What is the LCD for $^2/_8$ and $^1/_2$?

19. A regular hexagon has 9-cm sides. What is its perimeter?   cm

20. $4^3 = 4 \times 4 \times 4 =$

THURSDAY

1. Write the numeral eighty six point three.

2. If there are £0.60 (UK) to €1.00, how many euro would you get for £6.00 (UK)?

3. Name this shape.

4. Write the composite numbers between 11 and 20.

   ____, ____, ____, ____, and

5. The LCD for $^3/_4$ and $^2/_3$ is   .

6. Circle +4 on the number line.

7. $(8 \times 4) \div (16 \div 4) =$

8. This is the net of a

9. $^8/_{10} - ^3/_{10} =$

10. $(36 \div 3) + 3 =$

11. The time is 6.00 a.m. in Ireland and 9 a.m. in Kenya. What is the time difference?

12. Simplify $^{12}/_{16}$.

13. $6^2 =$

14. Draw a 180° turn.

 ▶

15. Tick the smallest ☐ $^2/_3$ ☐ $^3/_9$ ☐ $^4/_6$

16. What is the chance of picking a blue pen if your pencil case had 4 red and 6 blue pens?

                    in

17. The factors of 4 are   ,   and   .

18. Round 5.27. Is it 5.2 or 5.3?

19. 60% of €50 = €

20. A decagon has   sides.

1. $8^2 =$

2. $^4/_5 + ^3/_5 + ^4/_5 =$

3. Circle the approximate size of this angle.
   (a) *20°*   (b) *45°*   (c) *80°*

4. Is 494 divisible by 5?

5. Write one million, one thousand and ten as a numeral.

6. $40 \times ^4/_5 =$

7. $18 + a = 3 \times 9$ *so* a =

8. The factors of 8 are: ____ , ____ , ____ and ____ .

9. As a young architect you draw your new house plans. A large window measures 10 m long and needs to be drawn on paper as 10 cm long. What is your scale?
   ☐ *1:10*   ☐ *1:1*   ☐ *1:100*

10. What is the length of a wall shown as 7 cm in the same house?

11. 2.09 > 2.10   ☐ *true* ☐ *false*

12. Tick the smallest: ☐ $^1/_2$ ☐ $^2/_5$ ☐ $^9/_{10}$

13. $10 - 0.1 =$

14. Circle +6 on the number line.

15. $(16 \div 4) + 6 =$

16. Double 8.6.

17. How many B boxes would fit evenly into Box A?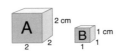

18. Write the prime number that comes after 19.

19. Round 6.09 to the nearest tenth.

20. The time is 10 p.m. in Ireland and 11 p.m. in Italy. What is the time difference?

1. $6^2 =$

2. $^2/_5 =$ ____ %

3. $^{11}/_5 - ^4/_5 =$

4. $(6 \times 5) - (2 \times 9) =$

5. $5 - 0.05 =$

6. $7 \overline{)294} =$

7. A circle has a diameter of 10 cm, what is its radius?
   ____ cm

8. Write the numeral thirty point six.

9. $3^3 = 3 \times 3 \times 3 =$

10. What is the meaning of 3 in 3 211 211?

11. A tetrahedron has:
    ____ faces
    ____ edges
    ____ vertices

12. Write the composite number that comes after 20.

13. 3, 9, 16, 24, ____

14. If a clock shows 6 o'clock, what is the angle between the hands?
    ____ °

15. What is the volume of this block?
    ____ cm³
    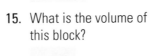
    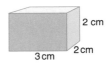

16. Round $3^4/_9$.

17. Is 244 divisible by 3?

18. Round 6.09 to one decimal place.

19. $24 \times ^3/_8 =$

20. A store has a 10% discount on all items. What should you pay for your solar-powered pencil sharpener, priced at €50?

    € ____

1. $9^2 =$

2. If a bucket contains 2 red balls, 5 green balls and 13 yellow balls, what chance have you of choosing a red ball?

    in

3. The factors of 9 are   ,   and   .

4. $200 - b = 110$ *so* $b =$

5. Tick the largest ☐ $^3/_{12}$ ☐ $^3/_4$ ☐ $^3/_6$

6. Simplify $^{15}/_{18}$.

7. Circle -4 on the number line.

8. Circle the size of this angle.
   (a) 90° (b) 10° (c) 120°

9. $1\,000 - 50 =$

10. What is the place value of 5 in 5 111 200?

11. Your new house plans show a wall 20 metres in length and is drawn on paper as 20 cm long. What is your scale?
    ☐ *1:1* ☐ *1:100* ☐ *1:2*

12. A square based pyramid has:

    faces

    edges

    vertices

13. A 20% discount on a €100 pair of shoes means you should pay €   .

14. $(9 \times 9) - 20 =$

15. The circumference of a circle is approximately how many times longer than the diameter?

16. How many B boxes would fit evenly into Box A?

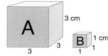

17. $29.5 \div 10 =$

18. If there are £0.60 (UK) to €1.00, how many euro would you get for £6.00 (UK)?

19. Round 20.54 to one decimal place.

20. Find the LCD for $^1/_3$ and $^3/_5$.

1. $7^2 =$

2. Your new house plan shows the lounge room window 8 m in length. You measure it on paper as 8 cm. What is the scale?
   ☐ *1:8* ☐ *1:100* ☐ *1:1*

On the circle diagram, label:

3. The *radius* 'A'.
4. The *diameter* 'B'.
5. The *circumference* 'C'.

6. $^4/_5 =$ %

7. $3 - 0.05 =$

8. $2^5 = 2 \times 2 \times 2 \times 2 \times 2 =$

9. 0.7, 0.8, 0.9,

10. Name this shape.

11. What is the probability of someone being born in August?

    in

12. $(6 \times 7) - (4 \times 5) =$

13. Write the numeral twelve point five.

14.

    Angle:

15. How would you write midnight in 24-hour time?

    hours

16. $30 \times ^5/_6 =$

17. Write one million, one thousand, one hundred and one as a numeral.

18. $41.2 \div 10 =$

19. Double 0.9.

20. Volume of a space 3 m wide by 4 m long by 2 m high? m^3

1. Write the prime numbers between 11 and 20.

    _____ , _____ , _____ and _____

2. Simplify $^{20}/_{25}$.

3. What is the ratio of boys to girls, if a class has 20 boys and 10 girls?

4. 600 + 900 =

5. Add brackets to this number sentence.

    6 x 4 + 3 ÷ 3 = 25

6. 29.3 ÷ 10 =

7. 10 − 0.2 =

8. Write the numeral one hundred and five point seven.

9. The factors of 10 are _____ , _____ , _____ and _____ .

10. The time is 4 p.m. in Ireland and 10 p.m. in India. What is the time difference?

11. Round 7.89 to the nearest tenth.

12. $^{3}/_{5}$ = _____ %

13. 100 ÷ 10 =

14. Is 153 divisible by 9? ☐ yes ☐ no

15. 1.2, _____ , 0.8, 0.6

16. This is the net of a

17.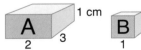

    How many B boxes fit evenly into Box A?

18. Will a square and a circle tessellate together?

19. Name this shape.

20. 10^4 =

1. Write the prime numbers between 21 and 30.

    _____ and _____

2. Tick the smallest   ☐ $^{3}/_{4}$ ☐ $^{3}/_{6}$ ☐ $^{2}/_{8}$

3. $1^{3}/_{4} + 2^{3}/_{4}$ =

4. 50% off a €300 item = € _____

5. Circle +3 on the number line.

6. Write one million, one hundred and ten thousand as a numeral.

7. 8 − 0.9 =

8. A cone has:

    _____ faces

    _____ edges

    _____ vertices

9. 7.70 > 7.09   ☐ true ☐ false

10. 21 is a multiple of 3. ☐ true ☐ false

11. 10^6 =

12. The circumference of a circle is approximately how many times longer than the diameter?

13. Name this triangle.

14. A room is 3 m long by 2 m wide and 3 m high. What is the volume of that room?

    _____ m^3

15. What is the ratio of boys to girls if there are 6 boys and 12 girls in a class?

16. Round $8^{3}/_{5}$.

17. Halve 10.5.

18. How many halves in 2?

19. $27 \times ^{3}/_{9}$ =

20. Write brackets to make this number sentence.

    3 x 8 − 5 x 2 = 14

WEDNESDAY

1. Write the composite numbers between 11 and 20.

   _____ , _____ , _____ , _____ and _____

2. If a clock shows 3 o'clock, what is the size of the angle between the hands?
   ☐ $45°$ ☐ $90°$ ☐ $180°$

3. Simplify $^8/_{24}$.

4. Write the numeral two hundred and sixteen point four.

5. What is the scale if a house plan shows a wall 3 cm long but is actually 3 m long?

6. Round 8.96. _____ (Nearest tenth)

7. $8\overline{)504}$ =

8. The factors of 12 are:

   _____ , _____ , _____ , _____ and _____

9. Is 252 divisible by 9?

10. $a + 25 = 100$ *so* a =

11. $4^1/_5 - {}^3/_5$ =

12. How many B boxes would fit into Box A?

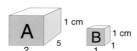

13. $16\ 500 + 9\ 500$ =

14. 12×11 =

15. 10^5 =

16. $10.6 \div 10$ =

17. Double $^1/_2$.

18. This is the net of a _____

19. Write one and one tenth as a decimal.

20. How many halves in 3?

THURSDAY

1. Write the composite numbers between 21 and 30.

   _____ , _____ , _____ , _____ , _____ , _____ and _____ .

2. Tick the largest   ☐ $^3/_6$ ☐ $^6/_9$ ☐ $^1/_3$

3. If there are £0.60 (UK) to €1.00, how many euro would you get for £30.00 (UK)?

4. $b - 45 = 55$ *so* b =

5. LCD for $^3/_4$ and $^5/_6$ is _____ .

6. Circle −4 on the number line.

7. Round 19.8.

8. $^4/_8$ = _____ %

9. The diameter of a circle is 7 cm. What is its radius?

   _____ cm

10. A cylinder has:

    _____ faces

    _____ edges

    _____ vertices

11. What is the probability of being born on a Monday?

    _____ in _____

12. $6^2/_5 - {}^4/_5$ =

13. Will a hexagon and a square tessellate together?

14. 26 is a multiple of 4.   ☐ *true* ☐ *false*

15. Write one million, one hundred and one thousand and one as a numeral.

16. Double $^1/_4$.

17. What is the ratio of girls to boys if a class has 5 girls and 20 boys?

18. $36 \times {}^4/_9$ =

19. If a €100 item is reduced by 25%, what is the new price? € _____

20. 2.97, 2.98, 2.99, _____

1. The factors of 15 are:

   _____ , _____ , _____ and _____

2. Write the numeral forty point five. _____

3. Circle the prime number.

   21   **23**   **25**

4. $^6/_8$ = _____ %

5. This is the net of a

   _____ .

6. 10 − 0.08 = _____

7. Add brackets to this number sentence.

   6 x 3 + 8 ÷ 2 = 22

8. 12.70 > 12.09   ☐ *true* ☐ *false*

9.

   Show this shape after a 180° turn.

10. Halve $^1/_2$. _____

11. 10^4 = _____

12. A jar contains 10 blue, 4 red and 6 white jelly beans. What is the chance of picking a blue one?

    _____ in _____

13. On your house plans a measurement of 8 m is indicated for a kitchen window. If the scale is 1:100, how long should you draw the line?

    _____

14. Name this shape.

    _____

15. What is the place value of 2 in 0.02? _____

16. Is 532 divisible by 9? _____

17. What is the size of this angle?

    _____

18. Tick the largest   ☐ $^1/_2$ ☐ $^9/_{12}$ ☐ $^1/_3$

19. 25% of 200 = _____

20. What is the volume of a box 50 cm by 30 cm by 20 cm? _____ cm^3

1. The factors of 16 are:

   _____ , _____ , _____ , _____ and _____ .

2. The time is 2 a.m. in Ireland and 10 a.m. in China. What is the time difference? _____

3. If the diameter of a circle is 9 cm, what is its radius?

   _____ cm

4. Share €160.00 with 8 people. € _____ each

5. 15 500 + 7 500 = _____

6. 1 − 0.04 = _____

7. Halve $^1/_4$.

8. How many B boxes fit into Box A?

   _____

9. Will a square and a rectangle tessellate together? _____

10. Circle −2 on the number line.

11. $7^1/_{10} − ^8/_{10}$ = _____

12. A tetrahedron has:

    _____ *faces*

    _____ *edges*

    _____ *vertices*

13. Name this shape.

    _____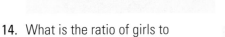

14. What is the ratio of girls to boys if there are 15 girls to 3 boys? _____

15. 25 x $^2/_5$ = _____

16. 25% of 300 = _____

17. 64 is a multiple of 9.   ☐ *true*   ☐ *false*

18. The LCD of $^7/_{10}$ and $^3/_4$ is _____ .

19. 8.1, 8.05, 8, _____ , 7.9, 7.85

20. How many halves in 5? _____

1. The factors of 18 are:

   _____ , _____ , _____ , _____ ,

   and _____ .

2. Write the numeral six hundred and twenty point four.

3. Simplify $^{20}/_{24}$.

4. $10^5 =$

5. Circle the composite number.

   29   **30**   **31**

6. Meaning of 9 in 0.09 is _____ .

7. $2\,000 - 350 =$

8.

   Draw after a 270° turn anticlockwise.

9. $^1/_3 =$ _____ %

10. 25% of 500 =

11. An octahedron has _____ faces.

12. How many B boxes would fit into Box A?

13. $5^2/_{10} - ^7/_{10} =$

14. 17, 34, 68, _____

15. $82.95 \div 10 =$

16. A bus timetable shows 8-minute intervals between each stop. If a bus leaves its depot at 9.02 a.m. and has 4 stops, what time does it reach its destination?

17. Add brackets to this number sentence.

    $9 \times 3 - 18 \div 2 = 18$

18. A cuboid has:

    faces _____

    edges _____

    vertices _____

19. 64 is a multiple of 8. ☐ *true* ☐ *false*

20. Write one million, one thousand, one hundred and eleven as a numeral.

1. The factors of 20 are:

   _____ , _____ , _____ , _____ ,

   and _____ .

2. $4 \times b = 36$ *so* b =

3. _____

   What is the size of this angle? _____ °

4. 25% of 800 =

5. This is the net of a _____

6. Simplify $^{18}/_{24}$.

7. $12 \times 9 =$

8. Is 621 divisible by 9? ☐ *yes* ☐ *no*

9. $9\overline{)342} =$

10. On a plan, how many centimetres should a wall be if its actual length is 12 m and the scale is 1:100?

    _____ cm

11. Tick the smallest ☐ $^9/_{10}$ ☐ $^2/_5$ ☐ $^6/_{10}$

12. Write five tenths as a decimal.

13. $4\,^8/_{10} + ^7/_{10} =$

14. How many halves in 4?

15. Double $^1/_4$.

16. $2 - 0.09 =$

17. $81 \times ^1/_9 =$

18. Share €40.00 with 16 people. € _____ each

19. $71.69 \div 10 =$

20. A regular octagon has a perimeter of 40 cm. What is the length of one side?

    _____ cm

1. The square root of 4 is   .
2. Write these decimals from smallest to largest.

   0.5   **0.75**   **0.05**

3. Your house plans are drawn using 1:100 as the scale. Measure this line and indicate the actual length in metres.

       m   ⊢————————⊣

4. $^3/_4$ kg =   g
5. 4.17 > 4.1   ☐ *true* ☐ *false*

6. 5 − 0.07 =
7. What is the area of a floor 8 m by 6 m? m^2
8. What is the angle between the hands of a clock that shows 9 o'clock?

   ☐ *45°*   ☐ *90°*   ☐ *9°*

9. Halve $^1/_4$.
10. Circle the prime number.

    27   **28**   **29**

11. Write one million, five hundred and fifty thousand as a numeral.

12.

    How many B boxes will fit into Box A?
13. The factors of 22 are:

        ,   ,   and
14. Write the numeral seven hundred and eighty point one.

15. (15 − 9) x (9 ÷ 3) =

16. 2^5 =

17. $^2/_3$ =   %
18. Write half past one in the morning as 24-hour time.   hours

19. 0.5, 5,   , 500, 5 000
20. This is the net of a

1. The square root of 36 is   .

2. How many thirds in 2?

3. 75% of 100 =
4. The angles in a square are all how many degrees?

       °

5. 6^2 =

6. Double 0.7.
7. Name this shape.

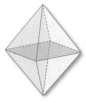

8. What is the ratio of boys to girls if a class has 10 boys and 20 girls?

9. Round 7.07 to the nearest tenth.

10. b x 12 = 108 *so* b =
11. Write these fractions from largest to smallest.

    $^7/_8$ $^1/_4$ $^3/_6$

12. $8^4/_8 + 2^7/_8$ =
13. What is the volume of this block?

        cm^3
14. The time is 1 p.m. in Ireland and 8 p.m. in Thailand. What is the time difference?

15. Circle −5 on the number line.

16. Is 433 divisible by 3?   ☐ *yes* ☐ *no*
17. Will a pentagon and a square tessellate together?

18. 80 x 50 =

19. 47.5 ÷ 10 =
20. A hat contains 7 names of boys and 8 names of girls. What is the chance of picking a girl's name?

        in

1. The square root of 9 is   .

2. A floor is 7 m by 4 m. Area =   m²

3. Write these decimals from largest to smallest.

    0.22   **0.2**   **0.02**

4. 75% of 200 =

5. What is the ratio of girls to boys if a class has 20 girls and 10 boys?

6. Round 29.35 to the nearest whole number.

7. Simplify $^{21}/_{24}$.

8. Draw a 90° turn clockwise.

9. $3^3 =$

10. $^1/_2$ kg =   g

11. Write six hundredths as a decimal.

12. Name this 3-D shape.

13. What is the radius of a circular lid with a 12 cm diameter?   cm

14. Circle the composite number.

    26   **29**   **31**

15. $8^1/_3 - ^2/_3 =$

16. The angles in an equilateral triangle are all   °.

17. How many faces on a cube?

18. $^1/_5 =$ %

19. $(16 - 7) - (12 \div 4) =$

20. What is the chance of picking a vowel from the alphabet?

    in

1. The square root of 49 is   .

2. How many B boxes fit into Box A?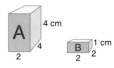

3. How many thirds in 3?

4. The angles in a rectangle are all how many degrees?   °

5. 300, 30, 3,

6. $300 \div c = 60$ c =

7. How many faces on a hemisphere?

8. $7\overline{)357} =$

9. Simplify $^{30}/_{36}$.

10. Write these fractions from largest to smallest.

    $^2/_5$ $^1/_{10}$ $^1/_2$

11. A square-based pyramid has:

    faces

    edges

    vertices

12. Write nine hundredths as a decimal.

13. $8.00 > 8.08$ ☐ *true* ☐ *false*

14. How many degrees?   °

15. 82 is a multiple of 2.   ☐ *true* ☐ *false*

16. $2 - 0.01 =$

17. 75% of 500 =

On the circle diagram label:

18. The *radius* 'A'.

19. The *diameter* 'B'.

20. The *circumference* 'C'.

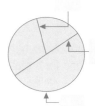

1. The square root of 16 is   .
2. Write these decimals from smallest to largest.

   0.4   **0.04**   **0.44**

3. Draw after a 180° turn.

   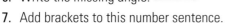

4. $1 - 0.98 =$
5. How many thirds in 5?
6. Write the missing angle.

7. Add brackets to this number sentence.

   $6 \times 3 \div 9 \times 2 = 1$

8. The average of these numbers is   .

   4   5   3   7   6

9. How many faces on an octahedron?
10. What is the place value of 2 in 3.812?

11. 1, 4, 9,   , 25
12. The factors of 24 are: ,   ,   ,

              ,   ,   , and   .

13. How many B boxes will fit into Box A?

14. $10^2 =$

15. $2\,000 - c = 1\,200$ *so* $c =$

16. 15% of €10 = €
17. This is the net of a.

    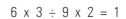

18. A floor needs tiling. How many square metres are needed for a room 6 m by 4 m?

    m²

19. $7^3/_{10} - {}^8/_{10} =$
20. If there are £0.60(UK) to €1.00, how many euro would you get for £15.00 (UK)?

1. The square root of 81 is   .
2. What is the ratio of boys to girls if there are 18 boys and 9 girls?
3. $^1/_5$ kg =   g
4. Meaning of 3 in 6.913?
5. Round 17.73 to the nearest tenth.
6. $10^5 =$
7. The next prime number after 19 is   .
8. $^4/_5 =$ %
9. Write the numeral sixteen point two five.
10. 15% of €50.00 = €
11. Write twelve hundredths as a decimal.
12. Faces on a cylinder.
13. Name this shape.

14. Write these fractions from smallest to largest.

    $^4/_5$ $^9/_{10}$ $^1/_4$

15. The angles in a rectangle are all   °.
16. Scale is 1:100. Your plan measures a wall as 9 cm, how many metres will the wall really be?

    m

17. A cylinder has:

    faces

    edges

    vertices

18. Write one minute past one in the afternoon as 24-hour time.

    hrs

19. 39 is a multiple of 3. ☐ *true* ☐ *false*
20. 8.009 < 8.02   ☐ *true* ☐ *false*

WEDNESDAY

1. The square root of 25 is _____ .
2. Write these decimals from largest to smallest.

    0.06   0.6   0.006

3. $1 - 0.96 =$

4. How many quarters in 2?

5. Write the missing angle.

6. $7.006 < 7.05$ ☐ *true* ☐ *false*

7. The average of these numbers is _____ .

    9   11   8   12   10

8.

    Draw a 270° turn clockwise.

9. The LCD for $^1/_8$ and $^2/_3$ is _____ .

10. $40\,000 - c = 10\,000$ *so* $c =$

11. $10^4 =$

12. A room is 5 m wide by 7 m long by 2 m high. What is the volume? _____ m³

13. The time is 3 a.m. in Ireland and 4 a.m. in Sweden. What is the time difference?

14. Colour to +3 on the thermometer.

15. Simplify $^{21}/_{27}$.

16. $^2/_5$ kg = _____ g

17. $3^4/_5 + 1^3/_5 =$

18. An octahedron has _____ faces.

19. What is the diameter of a circle with a radius of 11 cm?

    _____ cm

20. The circumference of a circle is how many times longer than the diameter?

THURSDAY

1. The square root of 64 is _____ .

2.

    How many B boxes will fit into Box A?

3.

    A   B   C   D

    Circle the angle which is 45°.

4. $1 - 0.95 =$

5. $^1/_8$ kg = _____ g

6. 1.85, 1.9, 1.95, _____

7. 15% of €40.00 = € _____

8. $2^4 =$

9. The next composite number after 20 is _____ .

10. $^1/_3 =$ _____ %

11. Write one million and ten as a numeral.

12. $2.003 < 2.030$ ☐ *true* ☐ *false*

13. Write the numeral fifty point seven two.

14. What is the ratio of 27 boys to 9 girls?

15. If a room was 7 m by 10 m, what is the floor area? _____ m²

16. Round 16.34 to the nearest tenth.

17. Colour to −4° on the thermometer.

18. Will a trapezium and a triangle tessellate together?

19. A cube has:

    faces

    edges

    vertices

20. Diameter of a circle = 3 cm. Therefore, circumference is about

    _____ cm.

1. Write $2\frac{1}{4}$ as an improper fraction.

2. $1 - 0.92 =$

3. What is the angle between the hands at 6 o'clock?
   °

4. The square root of 100 is   .

5. $3\frac{1}{3} - \frac{2}{3} =$

6. $c \div 5 = 100$ *so* $c =$

7. Write $\frac{1}{10}$ as a decimal.

8. Write the missing angle.
   °

9. The average of these numbers is   .

   5   8   6   4   7

10. 0, 1, 1, 2, 3, 5, 8,   , 21

11. The factors of 25 are   ,   and
    .

12. This is the net of a

13. If a radius is 60 cm, what is the diameter?
    cm

14. $11^2 =$

15. 9, 27, 81,

16. $\frac{3}{5}$ kg =   g

17. The next prime number after 23 is   .

18. What is the area of a piece of paper 20 cm by 10 cm?
    cm^2

19. How many faces on a square pyramid?

20. Write the numeral seventy point one five.

1. Write $4\frac{1}{2}$ as an improper fraction.

2. How many degrees in this angle?
   °

3. Order these decimals from smallest to largest.
   0.07   0.7   0.007

4. What is the perimeter of a block of land 25 m long by 20 m wide?   m

5. How many quarters in 3?

6. $5\frac{1}{5} - \frac{4}{5} =$

7. Write $\frac{5}{10}$ as a decimal.

8. Draw a 270° turn anticlockwise.

9. $(9 \times 4) \div (4 \times 3) =$

10. Name this shape.

11. Write one million, one hundred and eleven as a numeral.

12. $\frac{3}{5} =$ %

13.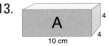

    How many B boxes would fit into Box A?
    °

14. The angles in a square are all   .

15. A triangular prism has:

    faces

    edges

    vertices

16. 70 is a multiple of 7. ☐ *true* ☐ *false*

17. Colour to −3 on the thermometer.

18. Will a square and a right angled triangle tessellate together?

19. 15% of 80 =

20. The LCD for $\frac{3}{4}$ and $\frac{1}{2}$ is   .

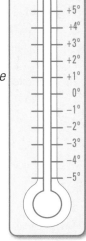

1. Write $3\frac{1}{3}$ as an improper fraction.

2. $y \div 4 = 40$ $\qquad$ $y =$

3. The square root of 25 is $\qquad$.

4. $10 - 0.98 =$

5. How many quarters in 4?

6. Write $\frac{1}{100}$ as a decimal.

7. $3\frac{7}{10} + 2\frac{7}{10} =$

8. The average of these numbers is $\qquad$.
   25 24 30 26 20

9. This is the net of a

10. Write these fractions from smallest to largest.
    $\frac{1}{2}$ $\qquad$ $\frac{6}{8}$ $\qquad$ $\frac{2}{6}$

11. Write ninety hundredths as a decimal.

12. $6\frac{1}{3} - \frac{2}{3} =$

13. $(100 - 50) - (4 \div 2) =$

14. 48 is a multiple of 4. ☐ *true* ☐ *false*

15. An octahedron has $\qquad$ faces.

16. What is the perimeter of a fence on a rectangular block 35 m in width and 55 m in length?

    $\qquad$ m

17. How many faces on a triangular prism?

18. The time is 2.20 p.m. in Ireland and 10.20 p.m. in Western Australia. What is the time difference?

19. What is the ratio of bananas to apples if a fruit bowl contains 15 bananas and 5 apples?

20. What is the chance of rolling a two on one die?

    $\qquad$ in $\qquad$

1. Write $2\frac{3}{4}$ as an improper fraction.

2. Order these decimals from largest to smallest.
   0.04 0.44 0.004

3. Name this shape.

4. Place value of 7 in 7 111 233?

5. What is the meaning of that 7?

6. $10 - 0.95 =$

7. Write $\frac{5}{100}$ as a decimal.

8. 25% of 60 =

9. $12^2 =$

10. Write the missing angle.

11. The factors of 26 are $\qquad$, $\qquad$,

    and $\qquad$

12. $\frac{1}{4}$ kg = $\qquad$ g

13. The next composite number after 24 is $\qquad$.

14.
    How many B boxes would fit into Box A?

15. $\frac{6}{8} =$ $\qquad$ %

16. $7.02 = 7.002$ ☐ *true* ☐ *false*

17. Write the numeral fifteen point zero two.

18. A pentagonal prism has:

    faces

    edges

    vertices

19. 3.3, 3.6, 3.9, $\qquad$

20. A hat contained 10 boys and 20 girls names. What is the chance of selecting a boy's name?

    $\qquad$ in $\qquad$

1. Write $^3/_2$ as a mixed number.

2. $5 - 0.91 =$

3. The square root of 9 is   .

4. Write $^6/_{10}$ as a decimal.

5. Write the missing angle.

6. y x 300 = 30 000 *so* y =

7. The radius of a circle is 3.5 cm. What is the diameter?   cm

8. The factors of 27 are   ,   ,

   and   .

9. This is the net of a

        .

10. Circle the prime number.

    23   25   27

11. Write one million, two hundred thousand as a numeral.

12. $2.2 - 0.3 =$

13. Draw a 180° turn clockwise.

14. Write $2^2/_3$ as an improper fraction.

15. Place value of 4 in 8.204?

16. Write the numeral ninety point zero three.

17. Name this shape.

18. Order these decimals from largest to smallest.

    0.08   1.8   0.8

19. How many quarters in 5?

20. 80, 150, 850,   , 77 850

1. Write $^7/_3$ as a mixed number.

2. What is the ratio of girls to boys if there are 15 girls and 5 boys?

3. Simplify $^{80}/_{100}$.

4. $7^2 =$

5. $8^8/_{10} + {}^{12}/_{10} =$

6. The square root of 49 is   .

7. Write $^{24}/_{100}$ as a decimal.

8. On a plan a wall measures 14 cm. The scale is 1:100. How long is the wall?

        m

9. The average of these numbers is   .

   10   3   0   7   5

10. $^1/_4$ kg =   g

11. How many fifths in 2?

12. Meaning of 3 in 9.253?

13.

   Volume =   cm³

14. What is the probability of picking a king from a deck of playing cards?

        in

15. $7.1 - 0.2 =$

16. 25% of 80 =

17. $^4/_5 =$ %

18. Write one million, nine hundred and nine thousand as a numeral.

19. A cuboid has:

    faces

    edges

    vertices

20. Colour to −1° on the thermometer.

1. Write $^5/_2$ as a mixed number.
2. What is the ratio of apples to pears if a fruit bowl contains 12 apples and 6 pears?

3. y x 700 = 70 000 *so* y =

4. Simplify $^{20}/_{50}$.

5. Write $^9/_{10}$ as a decimal.
6. Write the missing angle.

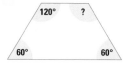

7. The factors of 28 are   ,   ,   ,

                    and   .

8. A cone has:

   faces

   edges

   vertices

9. 22 is a multiple of 4. ☐ *true* ☐ *false*

10.

    How many B boxes would fit Box A?

11. Write $1^3/_4$ as an improper fraction.
12. Colour to 0° on the thermometer.
13. Will a circle and a semicircle tessellate together?

15. $12^2 =$

On the circle diagram label:

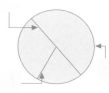

16. The diameter 'A'.
17. The circumference 'B'.
18. The radius 'C'.

19. How many fifths in 3?

20. 8.9 − 0.9 =

1. Write $^7/_4$ as a mixed number.

2. Write $^3/_{100}$ as a decimal.
3. Name this shape.

4. The square root of 16 is   .

5. The average of these numbers is   .

   4   9   8   3   6

6. This is the net of a

   .

7. $^4/_5$ kg =   g
8. Circle the composite number.

   11   12   13

9. 2, 2.9, 3.8, 4.7,
10. Order these decimals from smallest to largest.

    0.5   1.5   0.55

11. 8, 13, 21, 34,

12. $10^4 =$

13. $3^4/_7 + 5^6/_7 =$
14. What is the ratio of girls to boys if there are 12 girls and 4 boys?

15. Write the numeral twenty point four eight.

16. $^3/_4 =$ %

17. The angles in an equilateral triangle are all   .
18. 42 is a multiple of 6. ☐ *true* ☐ *false*

19. 6.4 − 0.9 =

20. Perimeter =   cm

1. Write $2^3/_4$ as an improper fraction.

2. $2 \div {}^1/_2 =$

3. The square root of 4 is _____.

4. $4^2 =$

5. Write $^7/_{10}$ as a decimal.

6. What is the diameter of a disc with a 25 cm radius?

   _____ cm

7. $y \times 800 = 80\ 000$ *so* $y =$

8. Name this shape.

   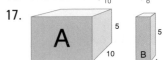

9. Write the numeral five point zero two.

10. The perimeter of a regular pentagon with 9 cm sides

    = _____ cm.

11. $40 + y = 50 \times 2$ *so* $y =$

12. $10 - 0.93 =$

13. Area of rectangle = _____ cm^2

14. Perimeter of rectangle = _____ cm

15. 1, 1.8, 2.6, 3.4, _____

16. The LCD for $^2/_{10}$ and $^3/_8$ is _____.

17.

    How many B boxes would fit into Box A?

18. Place value of 5 in 5 320 000.

19. $0.7 + 0.8 =$

20. Write $^8/_3$ as a mixed number.

1. Write $^9/_4$ as a mixed number.

2. Write the missing angle.

   _____ °

3. The radius of a circle is 5.2 cm. What is the diameter?

   _____ cm

4. The factors of 30 are _____, _____, _____, _____, _____, _____, _____ and _____.

5. This is the net of a _____.

6. Write one hundredth as a decimal.

7. What is the LCD for $^2/_5$ and $^1/_4$?

8. What is the ratio of boys to girls if there are 21 boys and 7 girls?

9. A jar contains 5 green marbles, 4 glass marbles and 11 red marbles. What is the probability of choosing a glass marble?

   _____ in _____

10. Write $^7/_{100}$ as a decimal.

11. What is the meaning of 4 in 3 428 028?

12. Double 2.7.

13. Draw as a 180° turn clockwise.

14. Write these decimals from smallest to largest.

    0.8   **0.08**   **8.8**

15. How many quarters in 2?

16. $^3/_4$ kg = _____ g

17. Round 23.88 to the nearest tenth.

18. $2 \div {}^1/_4 =$

19. $0.9 + 0.7 =$

20. Write $4^1/_3$ as an improper fraction.

WEDNESDAY

1. Write $5\frac{1}{2}$ as an improper fraction.

2. What is the place value of 2 in 8.712?

3. $400 \div y = 50$ $y =$

4. $2 \div \frac{1}{3} =$

5. Write these decimals from largest to smallest.

   0.01   **0.11**   **0.1**

6. How many halves in 6?

7. $5 - 0.92 =$

8. $\frac{2}{5}$ kg =   g

9. 15% of 100 =

10. $\frac{3}{5} =$ %

11. $(200 \times 10) - (5 \times 10) =$

12. How many degrees in this angle?

13. Halve 4.9.

14. Circle the prime number.

    5   **10**   **15**

15. Write $\frac{15}{100}$ as a decimal.

16. How many B boxes would fit into Box A?

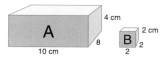

17. Area of rectangle =   cm²

18. Perimeter of rectangle =   cm

19. $10^6 =$

20. Write $\frac{11}{5}$ as a mixed number.

THURSDAY

1. Write $\frac{7}{2}$ as a mixed number.

2. $2 \div \frac{1}{5} =$

3. The square root of 64 is   .

4. If a wall is 5 m long and the scale is 1:100, how long is the wall in cm on the plan?

        cm

5. Round 12.27 to the nearest tenth.

6. Simplify $\frac{30}{40}$.

7. Write $\frac{2}{10}$ as a decimal.

8. 25% of 8 =

9. 3, 3.7, 4.4,   , 5.8

10. The angles in a triangle add up to   ° .

11. The diameter of a circle is 11 cm. What is the radius?

         cm

12. The time is 3.30 p.m. in Ireland and 10.30 a.m. in New York. What is the time difference?

13. $2.3 - 0.8 =$

14. The factors of 32 are   ,   ,   ,   ,   and   .

15. This is the net of a

16. Circle the composite number.

    17   **23**   **25**

17. 6.50 > 6.051   ☐ *true*   ☐ *false*

18. Write the numeral twelve point zero four.

19. $\frac{2}{3} =$ %

20. Write $2\frac{2}{3}$ as an improper fraction.

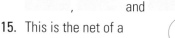

1. Circle the largest number.

   203 030   203 003

2. $3^2 + 4^2 =$

3. The temperature is −3 °C.
   What will it be if it rises by 6 °C?

4. Write one hundred and ten thousand as a numeral.

5. Write $2\frac{1}{4}$ as an improper fraction

   =

6. $\frac{1}{10} =$ %

7. $2 \div \frac{1}{4} =$

8. Draw 2 lines of symmetry.

9. Write $\frac{35}{100}$ as a decimal.

10. If there are $0.90 (US) to €1.00, how many euro for $1.80 (US)?

11. $5 \div 0.5 =$

12. Each angle in an equilateral triangle is   °.

13. The factors of 22 are   ,   ,

    and   .

14. Can a regular hexagon tessellate? ☐ yes ☐ no

15. $6^2 =$

16. 10% of €50.00 = €

17. Draw the net of a cube.

18. How many thirds in 2?

19. Write these fractions from smallest to largest.

    $\frac{2}{3}$ $\frac{1}{6}$ $\frac{5}{9}$

20. What is the chance of it raining today?

    (a) ☐ impossible (b) ☐ unlikely (c) ☐ even
    (d) ☐ very likely (e) ☐ certain

1. Circle the smallest number.

   145 022   154 020

2. Write $\frac{9}{2}$ as a mixed number.

3. What is the average of shoe sizes of 6, 7, 5?

4. Order from smallest to largest.

   100%   10%   50%

5. The square root of 36 is   .

6. 4, 14, 34, 64,

7. Area =   cm²

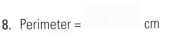

8. Perimeter =   cm

9. $\frac{2}{10} =$ %

10. Write the missing angle.
    °

11. Write these decimals from smallest to largest.

    4.5   4.05   4.55

12. $\frac{1}{5}$ kg =   g

13. What is the angle of North and East?
    °

14. Round 5.26 to one decimal place.

15. A tossed coin has a   in   chance of landing on a 'head'.

16. 10 x   = 8 x 5

17. $1 \div 0.5 =$

18. $\frac{2}{3} + \frac{2}{3} =$

19. Write the prime numbers between 11 and 20.

    ,   ,   and   .

20. What is the ratio of chocolates to jelly sweets if there are 3 chocolates and 12 jelly sweets?

1. Circle the largest number.

   560 040   **560 440**

2. $5^2 + 2^2 =$

3. Write $3\frac{1}{3}$ as an improper fraction.

4. Write two hundred and two thousand as a numeral.

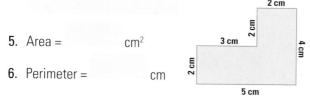

5. Area = ___ cm²

6. Perimeter = ___ cm

7. The cricket team scores 10, 30, 38, 30. What is the average?

8. $3 \div \frac{1}{4} =$

9. Write $\frac{7}{10}$ as a decimal.

10. $50\% > \frac{1}{2}$ ☐ true ☐ false

11. Each angle in a rectangle is ___ °.

12. The factors of 21 are ___ , ___ ,

    and ___ .

13. $\frac{3}{10} =$ ___ %

14. Draw the net of a cylinder.

15. Round 2.37 to the nearest tenth.

16. How many quarters in 4?

17. A rolled die has a ___ in ___ chance of landing on a '6'.

18. Write the composite numbers between 11 and 20.

    ___ , ___ , ___ , ___ ,

    and ___

19. A pair of €50 jeans have 20% off. What is the new price?   €

20. What is the chance of you going home from school early today?

    (a) ☐ impossible (b) ☐ unlikely (c) ☐ even
    (d) ☐ very likely (e) ☐ certain

1. Circle the smallest number.

   23 050   **203 050**

2. The temperature is –4 °C. What will it be if it rises by 5 °C?

3. Draw a double of this square. Show measurements.

4. How much has the area of the square increased by?

   (a) ☐ 12 (b) ☐ 4 (c) ☐ 6

5. Order from largest to smallest.

   25%   **20%**   **50%**

6. Write $\frac{7}{3}$ as a mixed number.

7. What is the average of these numbers?

   4   **6**   **2**

8. $70 + y = 140$ so $y =$

9. The square root of 25 is ___ .

10. What is the angle of North and South? ___ °

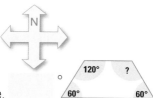

11. Write the missing angle.

12. Write these decimals from largest to smallest.

    2.005   **2.5**   **2.05**

13. $\frac{5}{10} =$ ___ %

14. $\frac{3}{5}$ kg = ___ g

15. Round 10.72 to one decimal place.

16. Write these fractions from largest to smallest.

    $\frac{1}{5}$ $\frac{9}{10}$ $\frac{1}{2}$

17. $2 \times$ ___ $= 4 \times 4$

18. $60 + 40 = 50 + y$ so $y =$

19. $1\frac{3}{5} + 1\frac{4}{5} =$

20. If there are $.90 (US) to €1.00, how many euro would you get for $9.00 (US)?

MONDAY

1. 250 g = $^1/_4$ kg = 0. _____ kg

2. Circle the smallest number.

       23 900   **203 900**

3. The temperature is –5 °C.
   What will it be if it rises by 3 °C?

4. The time is 10.20 a.m. in Ireland and
   3.20 p.m. in India. What is the time
   difference?

5. The angles in all triangles add up to
       °
   .

6. Draw 4 axes of
   symmetry
   on this square.

7. 3, 6, 9, 12   Rule = add

8. What is the ratio of boys to girls
   if there are 18 girls and 6 boys?

9. This is the net of a

   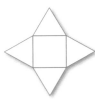

   .

10. In a class test the boys' top three
    marks were 80%, 70% and 60%.
    What is the average score?

11. (5 + c) = 3 x 5 *so* c =

12. $6^2 - 4^2$ =

13. Write $3^1/_4$ as an improper fraction.

14. 0.4 = _____ %

15. 5 ÷ $^1/_2$ =

16. Change $^{17}/_5$ to a mixed number.

17. Area = _____ m^2

18. Perimeter = _____ m

8 m
2 m
4 m
3 m
5 m
4 m

19. The square root of 81 is _____ .

20. A farm is 400 m by
    500 m, it equals _____ m^2.

TUESDAY

1. To measure a pencil would you use
   (a) a ruler or (b) a trundle wheel?

2. 500 g = $^1/_2$ kg = 0. _____ kg

3. The angles in all quadrilaterals add up to
   _____ °.

4. 10, 20, 30, 40   Rule = add

5. Write $^{10}/_3$ as a mixed number.

6. Write one million as a numeral.

7. What is the ratio of girls to boys if there are
   15 boys and 5 girls?

8. What is the angle of North and South?
       °

9. 0.7 = _____ %

10. 4 ÷ $^1/_3$ =

11. Write $^{43}/_{100}$ as a decimal.

12. Draw the net of a cone.

13. Order from smallest to largest.

        20%   **2%**   **45%**

14. A farm is 5 ha in size.
    It is 1 000 m by _____ m

15. The square root of 16 is _____ .

16. 20% of €80 = €

17. Round 5.89 to one decimal place.

18. 3 x 10 = 5 x y *so* y =

19. Circle the prime number.

        10   **13**   **16**

20. The chance of the next person who comes in being
    male is:
    (a) ☐ *impossible*   (b) ☐ *unlikely*
    (c) ☐ *even*   (d) ☐ *very likely*
    (e) ☐ *certain*

1. 750 g = $^3/_4$ kg = 0.＿＿＿ kg
2. If there are $.90 (US) to €1.00, how many euro would you get for $4.50 (US)?

3. 3, 5, 8, 12, ＿＿＿, 23
4. Circle the largest number.
   603 020　　　**630 020**
5. Write the missing angle.

6. ＿＿＿ % = 0.9

7. 5, 10, 15, 20　　Rule = ＿＿＿
8. What shape does the net make?

9. Find the average of
   6　　**8**　　**10**　　**12**
10. What angle is a?

11. $5^2 - 3^2 =$

12. Write $4^1/_3$ as an improper fraction.

13. Write $^3/_{10}$ as a decimal.
14. Order from largest to smallest.
    7%　　　**77%**　　　**70%**

15. A tossed coin has a ＿＿ in ＿＿ chance of landing on a 'tail'.

16.

A　　B　　C

If you turn the triangle 180°, what is its new position?

17. 80 + 40 = 60 x y *so* y = ＿＿＿
18. What is the ratio of apples to pears if there are 10 apples and 12 pears?

19. $6^3/_5 + 2^2/_5 =$

20. 6 x ＿＿ = 3 x 8

1. 200 g = $^1/_5$ kg = 0.＿＿＿ kg
2. Draw a shape double the size of this oblong and show the measurements.

3. How many times has the area increased by?
   (a) ☐ 2　(b) ☐ 4　(c) ☐ 6
4. The temperature is –3 °C. What will it be if it rises by 3 °C?

5. Parts of Australia are 8 hours ahead of GMT. If it is 9.15 a.m. in London, what time is it in Australia?

6. Write one million and ten as a numeral.
7. Write the missing angle.

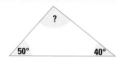

8. Draw one axis of symmetry on this pentagon.
9. 9, 11, 13, 11.

   The average is …

10. What angle is a?

11. If there are $.90 (US) to €1.00, how many euro would you get for $18.00 (US)?

12. 16, 12, 8, 4　　Rule = subtract

13. $8^2 - 2^2 =$
14. If you turn the triangle 180°, what is its new position?

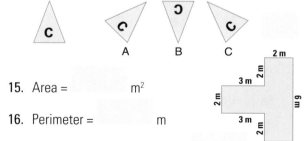
A　　B　　C

15. Area = ＿＿＿ m²

16. Perimeter = ＿＿＿ m

17. Write $^{14}/_4$ as a mixed number.

18. $10^4 =$

19. Round 6.08 to the nearest tenth.
20. What is the scale of a house plan if a wall is shown as 15 cm, and is actually 15 m?
    (a) ☐ *1:10*　(b) ☐ *1:100*　(c) ☐ *1:1 000*　(d) ☐ *100:1*

1. $600 \text{ g} = \frac{3}{5} \text{ kg} = 0.\underline{\quad} \text{ kg}$
2. List the possible outcomes of tossing a coin.

   _____ and _____
3. $100 \times a = 1\ 000$ *so* $a = \underline{\quad}$
4. Circle the smallest number.

   120 250   102 255
5. Round 6.073 to the nearest hundredth.
6. 45, 35, 25, 15   Rule = _____
7. $1\% = 0.01 = \underline{\quad}/_{100}$
8. 0.07, 0.08, 0.09, _____

The pie chart shows the number of brothers and sisters of 6th class pupils.

9. 32 pupils were surveyed.
   How many had 0 siblings?
10. Is the number of pupils who
    had 1 sibling the same as the
    number who had 3?

11. What percentage of the class had 2 siblings?
12. How many pupils had 5 siblings?
13. What shape does the net make?

14. If a car is travelling at
    60 km/hr, how far does it
    travel in 15 minutes? _____ km
15. Double $\frac{1}{2} = \underline{\quad}$
16. Write $2\frac{3}{4}$ as an improper fraction.
17. The square root of 9 is ____.
18. To measure the playground would you use
    (a) a ruler or (b) trundle wheel?
19. $8.08 > 8.1$ ☐ *true* ☐ *false*
20. A standard house plan is written in mm and the
    scale is generally 1 mm = 100 mm or 1:100.
    How long is a wall in mm if it measures 50 mm on
    the plan?

1. $333 \text{ g} = \frac{1}{3} \text{ kg} = 0.\underline{\quad} \text{ kg}$
2. If a car travels 6 km in 10 minutes,
   how far can it go in 1 hour? _____ km
3. $\frac{2}{3} + y = 1$ *so* $y = \underline{\quad}$
4. Round 5.534 to 2 decimal places.
5. Write one hundred and eleven thousand and eleven
   as a numeral.
6. The temperature is $-2\ °C$.
   What will it be if it rises by 5 °C?

7. $2\% = 0.02 = \underline{\quad}/_{100}$
8.

   Spin the cone on its axis clockwise
   90° and draw the new position for
   the letter A.
9. Draw 2 axes of symmetry in this
   rectangle.

5 cm

10. The diameter of this circle is _____ cm.
11. 6, 12, 18, 24   Rule = _____
12. Write $\frac{16}{3}$ as a mixed number.
13. Write $\frac{4}{10}$ as a decimal.
14. How many thirds in 3?
15. Draw the net of a triangular prism.
16. Order from smallest to largest.

    75%   57%   7%
17. Halve $\frac{1}{2}$.
18. $10^5 = \underline{\quad}$
19. If the scale is 1:100 on a plan, and a fence is 7 500 mm,
    how many millimetres should it measure on the plan?

    _____ mm
20. $16 \div \frac{1}{3} = \underline{\quad}$

WEDNESDAY

1. $800 \text{ g} = {}^4/_5 \text{ kg} = 0.\underline{\hspace{2cm}} \text{ kg}$
2. If there are \$.90 (US) to €1.00, how many euro for \$2.70 (US)?
3. 40% of €400.00 = €
4. Round 7.239 to 2 decimal places =
5. The angles in all quadrilaterals add up to \underline{\hspace{2cm}}.
6. $y =$
7. $9^2 + 2^2 =$
8. Write $5^1/_2$ as an improper fraction.
9. $5\% = \underline{\hspace{1cm}}/_{100} = 0.05$
10. Area = \underline{\hspace{1cm}} cm^2
11. Perimeter = \underline{\hspace{1cm}} cm
12. The square root of 4 is \underline{\hspace{1cm}}.
13. Parts of the USA are 6 hours behind GMT. If it is 4.20 p.m. in London, what time is it in the USA?
14. $y + {}^6/_{10} = 1$ so $y =$
15. Circle the composite number.

    11   **12**   **13**

16.

    E ▽ ▷

    Spin the triangle 90° anticlockwise. Draw the new position.

17. $4 \div {}^1/_4 =$
18. If a car travels 8 km in 10 minutes, how far could it travel in 1 hour?

    \underline{\hspace{2cm}} km

19. ${}^{17}/_6 =$
20. What is the chance of your teacher being happy today?

    (a) ☐ *impossible*   (b) ☐ *unlikely*   (c) ☐ *even*
    (d) ☐ *very likely*   (e) ☐ *certain*

THURSDAY

1. Round 4.075 to the nearest hundredth.
2. List the possible outcomes of rolling a die.

    \underline{\hspace{0.8cm}}, \underline{\hspace{0.8cm}}, \underline{\hspace{0.8cm}}, \underline{\hspace{0.8cm}}, \underline{\hspace{0.8cm}} and \underline{\hspace{0.8cm}}

3. Circle the largest number.

    750 050   **750 005**

4. What is the diameter of this circle?

    \underline{\hspace{2cm}} cm

5. ${}^{11}/_2 + y = {}^{31}/_2$ so $y =$
6. Simplify ${}^{12}/_{15}$.
7. ${}^9/_{100} = 0.09 = \underline{\hspace{1cm}} \%$
8. Draw the axes of symmetry on this hexagon.
9. 2.5, 5, 7.5, 10 \underline{\hspace{1cm}} Rule =
10. $6^2 - 5^2 =$
11. Write ${}^{19}/_5$ as a mixed number.
12. Write ${}^{65}/_{100}$ as a decimal.
13. How many eighths in 2?
14. Draw the net of a square-based pyramid.
15. What is the ratio of pens to pencils if there are 12 pens and 8 pencils?
16. ${}^1/_2 > {}^1/_3$ \underline{\hspace{1cm}} ☐ *true* ☐ *false*
17. $8^2 =$
18. If a car travels 10 km in 6 minutes, how far can it travel in 1 hour?

    \underline{\hspace{2cm}} km

19. Write one million, one thousand and one as a numeral.
20. A house plan scale is 1:100. A room measures 3 000 mm by 4 000 mm on the plan. How many square metres is the room?

    \underline{\hspace{2cm}} m^2

MONDAY

1. 1.5 + 2.5 =

2. $2^{1}/_{2}$ + y = 3 *so* y =

3. Spin the triangle 270° clockwise. Draw the new position.

4. $^{4}/_{5}$ kg = 0.8 kg =   g

5. 0.25 + 0.75 =

6. Round 2.375 to the nearest tenth.

7. Area =   cm²

8. Perimeter =   cm

9. What is the ratio of blue cars to white cars if there are 100 blue and 300 white cars?

10. Circle the largest.

    50% of 100   25% of 50

11. 233 m = $^{233}/_{1\,000}$ km = 0.   km

12. $9^{2}/_{3}$ + $9^{2}/_{3}$ =

13. 81, 72, 63, 54   Rule =

14. Write $3^{3}/_{5}$ as an improper fraction.

15. Double $^{1}/_{4}$.

16. 10% = $^{10}/_{100}$ = 0.

17. The square root of 36 is   .

18. What is the radius of this circle?
            cm

19. France is 1 hour ahead of GMT. If it is 11.10 a.m. in London what time is it in France?

20. If there are ¥116 to €1.00, how many euro would you get for ¥580?

TUESDAY

1. 3.25 + 4.5 =

2. A room measures 2 000 mm by 3 500 mm and the plan shows a scale of 1:100. On paper, it measures 20 mm by how many mm?

            mm

3. $^{1}/_{2}$ < $^{1}/_{5}$ ☐ *true* ☐ *false*

4. The average of these numbers is   .
    20   30   50   20

5. List the possible outcomes of rolling a die.

            ,   ,   ,   ,   and

6. Circle the largest.
    10% of 80   5% of 100

7. 505 m = $^{505}/_{1\,000}$ km = 0.   km

8.
    If you turn the triangle 90° anticlockwise, what is the new position?

9. Round 9.539 to 2 decimal places.

10. Draw the axis of symmetry on the trapezium.

11. If there are ¥116 to €1.00, how many euro would you get for ¥232?

12. Write $^{22}/_{5}$ as a mixed number.

13. $^{11}/_{100}$ = 0.11 =   %

14. Write $^{20}/_{100}$ as a decimal.

15. Draw the net of a cuboid.

16. Order from smallest to largest.
    90%   9%   99%

17. Halve $^{1}/_{4}$.

18. Write four hundred and thirty-two thousand and thirty-two as a numeral.

19. $6^{1}/_{2}$ + y = 7 *so* y =

20. If a car travels 9 km in 10 minutes, how far can it go in 1 hour?   km

1. 6.3 + 2.1 =

2. Circle the smallest.

   10% of 70   **20% of 50**

3. 15% of €20.00 = €

4. 925 m = $\frac{925}{1\,000}$ km = 0.   km

5. Draw another rectangle with the measurements reduced by one half. (1:2)

   8
   6

6. By how many times has the area been reduced?

   ☐ *4*   ☐ *1*   ☐ *8*

7. 1.5, 3.5, 5.5, 7.5   Rule =

8. y = y° 100°

9. Round 12.079 to 2 decimal places.

10. How many halves in 10?

11. $3 \div \frac{1}{4}$ =

12. $10^2 - 8^2$ =

13. If the radius is 6.5 cm, what is the diameter of a circle?

    cm

14. y x 10 = 5 *so* y =

15. 100% = $\frac{100}{100}$ =

16. A room measures 5 000 mm by 6 800 mm. A plan has a scale of 1:100. On paper it will measure 50 mm by …

    mm

17. Simplify $\frac{20}{24}$.

18. Write the missing angle.

    90°
    110°   ?
    50°

19. 2^4 =

20. Round 3.428 to the nearest hundredth.

1. 8.75 + 10.75 =

2. If a car travels 12 km in 10 minutes, how far can it go in 1 hour?

   km

3. Parts of Africa are 2 hours ahead of GMT. If it is 10.30 p.m. in London, what time is it in Africa?

4. 0.01 > 0.0009   ☐ *true* ☐ *false*

5. Area =   m²

6. Perimeter =   m

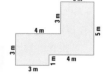
3 m
3 m
4 m
5 m
3 m
1 m   4 m
3 m

7. 15% of €40.00 = €

8. $\frac{1}{2}$ kg = 0.5 kg =   g

9. Circle the smallest.

   20% of 10   **1% of 100**

10. Draw a double (2:1) of this oblong, showing measurements.
    2
    3

11. How many times has the area increased by?

12. y x 6 = 12 *so* y =

13. 0.04 = $\frac{4}{100}$ =   %

14. 870 m = $\frac{870}{1\,000}$ km = 0.   km

15. What is the radius of a circle with a diameter of 23 cm?   cm

16. Draw the axes of symmetry in the parallelogram.

17. Write ten million as a numeral.

18. Draw the net of a cone.

19. 2^6 =

20. $6 \div \frac{1}{4}$ =

1. 2.05 + 6.7 =
2. 0.5 = $^1/_2$ ☐ *true* ☐ *false*
3. Draw a net of a cone.

4. Parts of South America are 4 hours behind GMT. If it is 2 a.m. in London, what time is it in South America?

5. Orla scored $^9/_{10}$ in a spelling test. Write this as a percentage.

      %

6. Change $10^3/_7$ to an improper fraction.

7. What is the meaning of 2 in 7.002?

8.

      A   B   C

   If you turn the triangle 270° clockwise, what will the new position be?

9. What is the probability of selecting a vowel from the alphabet?

      in

10. 3.2 − 0.3 =
11. A farm block is 400 m by 500 m. What area is it?   m²
12. y =   y° 45°
13. $^{37}/_{10} + ^{25}/_{10}$ =
14. Double 2.7.
15. 1, 1.8, 2.6, 3.4,
16. 820 m = $^{820}/_{1\,000}$ km = 0.   km
17. What is the radius of a circle with a diameter of 17 cm?   cm
18. 16   2 = 32
19. Which is the best value for money?
    ☐ *500 g coffee at €2.50*
    ☐ *1 kg coffee at €4.50*

20. 100, 81, 64, 49   Rule =

1. 4.25 + 6.15 =
2. Draw a double of this shape and write new measurements on all sides.

3. 2 − y = $1^1/_3$ *so* y =
4. Circle the largest.
   50% of 24   **10% of 100**

5. 10   15 = 25
6. 25% of €40.00 = €
7. Which is the best value for money?
   ☐ *€50 jeans with 75% off*
   ☐ *€30 jeans with 30% off*
8. If there are ¥116 to €1.00, how many euro would you get for ¥1 160?

9. Write $2^7/_8$ as an improper fraction.
10. 10^6 =
11. The square root of 16 is   .
12. Halve 3.8.
13. Round 18.795 to 2 decimal places.
14. A house plan has a scale of 1:100. A wall measures 110 mm on the plan. What is the actual length of the wall?

      m

15. 8.3 − 0.5 =
16. Write ten million, one hundred and one thousand as a numeral.
17. Round 8.069 to the nearest hundredth.

18. Draw the axes of symmetry on the oval.

19. 15% = 0.
20. A car is travelling at 100 km/hr. How far can it travel in $^1/_2$ of an hour?

      km

WEDNESDAY

1. 3.2 + 6.15 =

2. Round 2.349 to the nearest hundredth.

3. Vanessa scored $^6/_{10}$ in a maths test. Write this as a percentage.   %

4. 575 m = $^{575}/_{1\,000}$ km = 0.   km

5. Draw this shape at half size and write new measurements on all sides.

6. The LCD for $^1/_4$ and $^3/_{10}$ is   .

7. Halve 4.9.

8. It is 10.15 p.m. in Ireland and 11.15 p.m. in France. What is the time difference?

9. 80   45 = 35

10. 3.3, 6.6, 9.9   Rule =

11. The square root of 49 is   .

12. The scale is 1:100. A house plan shows a wall measuring 110 mm on the plan. What is the actual length in m?

                m

13. Write $^{12}/_{100}$ as a decimal.

14. Order from smallest to largest.

    45%   **4.5%**   **54%**

15.

    Turn the rectangle 180°. Draw the new position.

16. Area =   m²

17. Perimeter =   m

18. $^{29}/_{100}$ =   %

19. A farm block is 800 m by 500 m. What area is it?   m²

20. 8.9 − 0.9 =

THURSDAY

1. 4.525 + 3.2 =

2. Circle the smallest.

    2% of 50   **5% of 100**

3. a =

4. 1, 4, 9,   , 25

5. 905 m = $^{905}/_{1\,000}$ km = 0.   km

6. Simplify $^{15}/_{20}$.

7. 7^2 =

8. 45   9 = 5

9. Which is the best value for money?
    ☐ $^1/_4$ kg apples for € 1.20
    ☐ $^1/_2$ kg apples for € 2.50

10. Write $^{17}/_2$ as a mixed number.

11. If there are $0.60 (US) to € 1.00, how many euro would you get for $6.30 (US)?

12. Round 10.054 to 2 decimal places.

13. Draw the net of a triangular prism.

14. How many fifths in 8?

15. A car is travelling at 100 km/hr. How far can it travel in $^3/_4$ of an hour?

                km

16. 4 ÷ $^1/_5$ =

17. 25% of € 100.00 = €

18. 9 $^1/_2$ + y = 10 *so* y =

19. $10^2 + 5^2$ =

20. Which shapes have symmetry?

1. 8.65 − 2.14 =

2. 2.02 > 2.1   ☐ *true* ☐ *false*

3. Kate scored $^5/_{10}$ in a times table test. Write this as a percentage.

         %

4. 9.3 − 0.9 =

5. What is the average of 15, 30, 15, 20?

6. The LCD for $^1/_4$ and $^3/_5$ =

7. 755 m = $^{755}/_{1\,000}$ km = 0.   km

8.

    Turn the rectangle 90°clockwise. Draw the new position.

9. 6   8 = 14

10. Which is the best value for money?
    ☐ *250 g of grapes at €2.00*
    ☐ *200 g of grapes at €1.50*

11. y x 3 = $^3/_5$ *so* y =

12. 3, 6, 9, 12   Rule =

13. Circle the largest.
    20% of 50   **25% of 60**

14. 12 500 − 6 500 = a *so* a =

15. Write $^{16}/_3$ as a mixed number.

16. Simplify $^{50}/_{100}$.

17. Draw the axes of symmetry on the equilateral triangle.

18. 2 ÷ $^1/_5$ =

19. What is the ratio of Cork football fans to Waterford fans if there are 1 000 Cork fans and 200 Waterford fans?

20. If there are $0.90 (US) to €1.00, how many euro would you get for $7.20 (US)?

1. 7.25 − 3.02 =

2. 2.3 + 0.8 =

3. 4   7 = 28

4. Write $3^2/_3$ as an improper fraction.

5. 10% of 100 =

6. The square root of 25 is   .

7. The LCD for $^2/_3$ and $^1/_6$ =

8. Write $^{30}/_{100}$ as a decimal.

9. (4 x 9) = 6^2 ☐ *true* ☐ *false*

10. a =

11. Draw the net of a cube.

12. $5^2 + 6^2$ =

13. Circle the largest.
    110 055   **110 050**

14. If you double the size of this rectangle, how many times has the area increased by?

                        3
                     5

15. 50% = 0.5   ☐ *true* ☐ *false*

16. Write the prime numbers between 1 and 20.

    ,   ,   ,   ,
    ,   ,   and

17. Is 48 a multiple of 7?

18. 5 x   = 10 x 3

19. 2^5 =

20. A car is travelling at 50 km/hr. How far can it travel in 30 minutes?   km

1. 9.79 – 2.53 =

2. Simplify $^{14}/_{18}$.

3. 5.05 + 2.91 =

4. 0.99 =   %

5. Draw as a 270° turn anticlockwise.

6. 950 m = $^{950}/_{1\,000}$ km = 0.   km

7. 20   3 = 17

8. 8 = y + 6 $^1/_2$ *so* y =

9. What is the probability of choosing a red marble from a jar if there were 15 blue, 10 red and 25 green marbles?

    in

10. Round 25.093 to 2 decimal places.

11. Draw the axis of symmetry on the trapezium.

12. 3 ÷ $^1/_4$ =

13. Circle the largest.

    590 145   **509 145**

14. Write ten million and ten as a numeral.

15. 50% = 0.75   ☐ *true* ☐ *false*

16. What is the ratio of pens to pencils if there are 10 pens and 15 pencils?

17. Place value of 9 in 904 711 is   .

18. What is the area of this floor?

    8 m

    KITCHEN 4 m

    m²

19. Write $^{18}/_4$ as a mixed number.

20. 60% of € 110.00 = €

1. 6.99 – 2.08 =

2. James scored $^{10}/_{10}$ in a spelling test. Write this as a percentage.   %

3. Which is the best value for money?
    ☐ *750 g of flour at € 1.00*
    ☐ *500 g of flour at 75c*

4. 2.2, 4.4, 6.6   Rule =

5. Circle the largest.
    75% of 60   50% of 80

6. Round 0.143 to the nearest hundredth.

7. 1.22 =   %

8. 0, 1, 1, 2, 3, 5, 8, 13,

9. Write $2^6/_7$ as an improper fraction.

10. Place value of 4 in 542 067 is

                    .

11. Write the composite numbers between 1 and 20.

    ,   ,   ,   ,   ,

    ,   ,   ,   ,

    and

12. $6^3/_4 + 3^3/_4$ =

13. y x 10 = 50 *so* y =

14.

    Turn the cylinder 270° clockwise. Draw the new position.

15. 2.75 + 5.03 =

16. 18   3 = 6

17. 3 ÷ $^1/_2$ =

18. Is 48 a multiple of 6?

19. 6 x   = 9 x 4

20. A fast red car is travelling at 90 km/hr. How far can it travel in 20 minutes?

    km

MONDAY

1. 7.95 − 2.05 =

2. The LCD for $^3/_4$ and $^2/_3$ =

3. 4 + ⁻8 =

4. 0.5 x 0.5 =

5. y + 2 = 2$^3/_5$ so y =

6. Sarah scored 75% in a piano exam. Write this as a decimal.

7. 9.6 − 0.9 =

8.

Turn the rectangle 450° clockwise. Draw the new position.

9. 545 m = $^{545}/_{1\,000}$ km = 0._____ km

10. 12 ____ 3 = 36

11. Round 7.37 to the nearest tenth.

12. $^{135}/_{100}$ = 1.35 = _____ %

13. Which is the best value for money?
    ☐ € 40 shirt with 25% off
    ☐ € 50 shirt with 30% off

14. What is the probability of choosing a month beginning with J from a hat?

    _____ in

15. Write one million and eleven as a numeral.

16. 98, 94, 90, 86 _____ Rule =

17. Circle the largest.
    10% of 70 _____ **50% of 16**

18. 10 ÷ $^1/_5$ =

19. If a car takes 10 minutes to travel 10 km, how fast is it going?

    _____ km/hr

20. What is the perimeter of this shape?

    _____ m

TUESDAY

1. 8.29 − 6.05 =

2. 9 ____ 18 = 27

3. $^{31}/_7$ = _____ (mixed number)

4. 7 ÷ $^1/_2$ =

5. Write $^{500}/_{1\,000}$ as a decimal.

6. Draw the net of a square-based pyramid.

7. $4^2/_7$ + y = 5 so y =

8. If you measure the length of a fence as 8 m and draw it on a plan with a scale of 1:100, what will be its length on the plan?

    _____ cm

9. Circle the largest.
    252 891 _____ **2 052 891**

10. 2.02 = _____ %

11. What is the diameter of a circle if the radius is 4 cm?

    _____ cm

12. 65% = 0.6 ☐ true ☐ false

13. Is 24 a multiple of 2?

14. If a clock shows 3 o'clock, what is the size of the angle between the hands?

    _____ °

15. If you halve the measurements of this shape, how many times will the new shape fit into this shape?

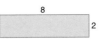

16. 6 + ⁻3 =

17. 0.2 x 0.5 =

18. Draw the axis of symmetry on this isosceles triangle.

19. 25% of 120 =

20. 12 x _____ = 8 x 3

WEDNESDAY

1. 5.87 – 2.43 =

2. The following are shoe sizes of basketball players.

   12   11   13   14   10

   What is the average?

3. 7 + ⁻6 =

4. 0.3 x 0.4 =

5. 983 m = $^{983}/_{1\,000}$ km = 0.   km

6. 64   8 = 8

7. 80, 65, 50, 35   Rule =

8.

   Turn the rectangle 270° anticlockwise. Draw the new position of the W.

9. Simplify $^{20}/_{30}$.

10. y x 50 = 25 *so* y =

11. Circle the largest.

    90% of 90   80% of 100

12. Draw a 90° turn anticlockwise.

13. $^{81}/_{10}$ =

14. Write $^{750}/_{1\,000}$ as a decimal.

15. 5% = 0.5   ☐ *true* ☐ *false*

16. a =

17. 0.97, 0.98, 0.99,

18. Write one hundred and eleven thousand and ten as a numeral.

19. Write $^{25}/_{4}$ as a mixed number.

20. Is 45 a multiple of 7?

THURSDAY

1. 9.76 – 4.52 =

2. David scored 89% in a maths test. Write this as a decimal.

3. Circle the prime number.

   4   7   9

4. 8.2 – 0.8 =

5. $9^{3}/_{4} + {}^{1}/_{2}$ =

6. 9.2   1.2 = 8

7. Which is the best value for money?

   ☐ €*800 table with 50% off*

   ☐ €*600 table with 30% off*

8. 500, 50, 5,

9. 9^2 =

10. Draw the net of a cylinder.

11. 5 + ⁻7 =

12. 9 ÷ $^{1}/_{3}$ =

13. Circle the largest.

    250 893   205 893

14. 5 x   = 10 x 3

15. If your new car travels 8 km in 10 minutes, how fast is it going?

    km/hr

16. 3 x   = 18 ÷ 3

17. What is the meaning of 3 in 3 211 744?

18. 0.7 x 0.3 =

19. Write $5^{2}/_{5}$ as an improper fraction.

20. How many B boxes will fit into Box A?

1. 0.5 x 0.4 =

2. 4 + ⁻8 =

3. Juliette scored 45% in a French test.
   Write this as a decimal.

4. 1 m 12 cm = $1^{12}/_{100}$ m = 1. ____ m

5. 9.09 < 9.9   ☐ *true* ☐ *false*

6. 9.1 − 0.8 =

7. 2 ____ 13 = 26

8. 30% of €40.00 = €

9. Which is the best value for money?
   ☐ *€80 dress with 20% off*
   ☐ *€90 dress with 33% off*

10. 16 ÷ $^1/_4$ =

11. $8^3/_4 + ^1/_2$ =

12. Write $^{350}/_{1\,000}$ as a decimal.

13. Circle the largest.
    5 052 040   **5 500 040**

14. Round 6.97 to the nearest tenth.

15. 9.65 − 2.34 =

16. 7.2 − y = 6.8 *so* y =

17.

    Spin the triangle 180° clockwise. Draw the new
    position.

18. 2.4, 4.8, 7.2   Rule =

19. Double $^3/_5$.

20. What is the radius of a circle if the diameter is 4 cm?

    ____ cm

1. 0.6 x 0.3 =

2. If you draw a 6 m wall with a scale of 1:100, how
   many mm will it be on the plan?

   ____ mm

3. The LCD for $^3/_4$ and $^1/_6$ is ____ .

4. 12.3 − 0.8 =

5. 6 + ⁻2 =

6. Write ten million, one hundred
   and ten thousand as a numeral.

7. 2 m 15 cm = $2^{15}/_{100}$ m = 2. ____ m

8. If a car travels 12 km in 10 minutes, how fast is it
   going?

   ____ km/hr

9. What is the chance of selecting an even number
   from a pack of cards?

   ____ in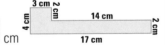

10. Draw the reflection.

11. 500 ____ 5 = 100

12. 3.5 + y = 5 *so* y =

13. 3.3, 6.6, 9.9   Rule =

14. Area = ____ cm²

15. Perimeter = ____ cm

16. Circle the largest.
    20% of 50   **60% of 25**

17. Halve $^4/_{10}$.

18. 8.96 − 1.05 =

19. 1, 3, 9, 27, ____ , 243

20. Write $^{63}/_{1\,000}$ as a decimal.

1. 0.4 x 0.8 =

2. 2 + ⁻7 =

3. Simplify $^{21}/_{28}$.

4. 4.82 + 2.07 =

5. An octahedron has _____ faces.

6. Mark scored 58% in a violin exam. Write this as a decimal.

7. $^4/_5 > ^2/_{10}$ ☐ true ☐ false

8. a =

9. 5 m 56 cm = $5^{56}/_{100}$ m = 5. _____ m

10. Draw the axes of symmetry on this pentagon.

11. 40 _____ 35 = 5

12. 4.0 + y = 7.5 so y =

13. A dodecahedron has _____ faces.

14. Tick the largest.
    ☐ 15% of 100
    ☐ 50% of 40

15. 1 = _____ %

16. Which of the following numbers is a prime number? 6, 9, 11

17. 10 ÷ $^1/_3$ =

18. Circle the largest.

    700   250   7 000   520

19. Halve $^1/_5$.

20. 20% = 0.25 ☐ true ☐ false

1. 0.1 x 0.9 =

2. ⁻8 + 2 =

3. Draw the axes of symmetry on this hexagon.

4. 4 m 28 cm = $4^{28}/_{100}$ m = 4. _____ m

5. 14 _____ 14 = 28

6. Which is best value for money?
    ☐ €1 000 bed with 15% off
    ☐ €900 bed with 10% off

7. $^3/_6 > ^1/_3$ ☐ true ☐ false

8. $4^1/_2 + ^3/_4$ =

9. What is the chance of selecting an odd number from a pack of cards?

10. 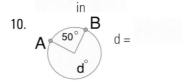 d =

11. 3.5 − 0.9 =

12. 10^2 =

13. 5.03 + 2.84 =

14. Draw the net of a tetrahedron.

15. What is the place value of 0 in 2 076 543?

16. 8 ÷ $^1/_5$ =

17. 18 − y = 9 so y =

18. 6% = 0.6 ☐ true ☐ false

19. Is 64 a multiple of 4?

20. Round 0.777 to the nearest tenth.

1. $0.6 \times 0.5 =$

2. $8 + {}^-3 =$

3. A car travels at 100 km/hr for 350 km. How many hours is the trip?   hrs

4. $200 - 50 \div (40 \div 8) =$

5. 5 m 15 cm = $5^{15}/_{100}$ m = 5.   m

6. 16   4 = 4

7. $6^1/_3 + 2^2/_3 =$

8. C =

9. What is the average of 150, 100, 150, 200?

10. Write $^{155}/_{1\,000}$ as a decimal.

11. Tick the largest.
    ☐ 7 502 250
    ☐ 7 205 250

12. Draw the net of a cube.

13. $12.63 + 12.04 =$

14. $3 - y = 2.7$ *so* y =

15. 1.1, 2.2, 3.3   Rule =

16. $2.7 > {}^{28}/_{10}$ ☐ true ☐ false

17. Draw a 180° turn clockwise.

18. What is the probability of selecting a 'face' card from a pack of playing cards?

                    in

19. Double 7.7.

20. Which is the best value for money?
    ☐ *500 g tea at €2.00*
    ☐ *750 g tea at €2.90*

1. 12   4 = 48

2. Is 27 a multiple of 7?

3. 6 x   = 3 x 8

4. $(600 - 200) \div (10 \div 2) =$

5. The LCD for $^3/_{10}$ and $^1/_6$ =

6. 18, 38, 78, 158,

7. 750 g = $^3/_4$ g = 0.   kg

8. Which of the following numbers is a prime number? 16, 17, 18

9. a =

10. $9 - y = 8.5$ *so* y =

The pie chart shows the number of pets owned by 6th Class pupils.

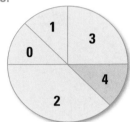

11. 24 pupils were surveyed. How many had 3 pets?

12. Is the number of pupils who had 0 or 1 pets the same as the pupils who had 3 pets?

13. What fraction of the class had 2 or 4 pets?

14. What percentage of the class had 3 pets?

          %

15. How many pupils had 2 pets?

16. $32 = 2^a$ *so* a =

17. $4 + {}^-6 =$

18. How many edges on an octagon?

19. Write $^5/_{1\,000}$ as a decimal.

20. 8, 16, 24   Rule =

WEDNESDAY

1. $^-9 + 3 =$

2. $(4 \div 2) + (6 \times 5) =$

3. The LCD for $^2/_{10}$ and $^3/_4$ is _____ .

4. $0.7 \times 0.2 =$

5. Write one million, nine hundred and nine thousand as a numeral.

6. $900 - 325 =$

7. 7 m 98 cm = $7^{98}/_{100}$ = 7. _____ m

8. 27 _____ 6 = 33

9. Halve 0.5.

10. Which is best value for money?
    - ☐ *12 apples at €2.40*
    - ☐ *15 apples at €2.99*

11. $3.5 \neq 3^1/_2$ ☐ *true* ☐ *false*

12. Double this shape.
    Write the new
    measurements
    on each side.

13. How many faces on a hemisphere?

14. Tick the largest.
    - ☐ *9 452 980*
    - ☐ *9 450 980*

15. $100\% = ^{100}/_{100} =$

16. Draw the reflection. **325**

17. $15.95 - 7.42 =$

18. Area = _____ m^2

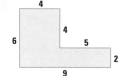

19. Perimeter = _____ m

20. $70\% = 0.07$ ☐ *true* ☐ *false*

THURSDAY

1. Simplify $^{10}/_{15}$.

2. What is the average of 6, 8, 10, 12?

3. Name this shape.

4. $y \times 6 = 24$ *so* $y =$

5. $0.3 \times 0.5 =$

6. $2 + ^-5 =$

7. 18 _____ 0 = 18

8. Write $^{30}/_{1\,000}$ as a decimal.

9. $^5/_6 = ^{15}/_{18}$ ☐ *true* ☐ *false*

10. If you draw a 90 mm line for a wall on a plan of 1:100, how many m is the wall?

    _____ m

11. Tick the largest.
    - ☐ *75% of 20*
    - ☐ *20% of 50*

12. $7 \div ^1/_3 =$

13. $11^2 =$

14. Name this shape.

15. How may axes of symmetry does it have?

16. What is the chance of it raining today?
    - ☐ *impossible* ☐ *unlikely* ☐ *likely* ☐ *certain*

17. $8^3/_5 + 1^3/_5 =$

18. $90\% = 0.9$ ☐ *true* ☐ *false*

19. $5 \times$ _____ $= 50 \div 5$

20. $3^1/_4 + y = 3^3/_4$ *so* $y =$

1. $4 + {}^-9 =$
2. What is the chance of picking a spade from a deck of cards?   in
3. Name this triangle.

4. $0.8 \times 0.2 =$

5. 5 m 24 cm = $5^{24}/_{100}$ = 5.

6. 26   24   50 = 100

7. Write $^9/_{1\,000}$ as a decimal.

8. $2.3 - 0.9 =$
9. Tick the largest.   ☐ 9 850 725
                              ☐ 9 800 925

10. Change $4^3/_7$ to an improper fraction.

11. Round 6.437 to 2 decimal places.

12. $7 \times y = 70$ *so* $y =$

13. What is the radius of a biscuit tin with a 30-cm diameter?   cm

14. 25, 36, 49   Rule =

15. $7^3/_4 + 2^1/_4 =$
16. Which is best value for money?
    ☐ *250 g corn at 50c*
    ☐ *500 g corn at 95c*

17. 4 kg 450 g = $4^{450}/_{1\,000}$ kg = 4.

18. A cube has   *faces*

                   edges

                   vertices.

19. $100\,000 = 10^a$ *so* $a =$
20. Draw the axes of symmetry on the rectangle.

1. $0.7 \times 0.9 =$

2. $3 + {}^-2 =$

3. 100   25   50 = 25

4. Write $^{90}/_{1\,000}$ as a decimal.
5. What is the meaning of 2 in 3 214 579?

6. $5.24 + 15.71 =$

7. The LCD for $^3/_8$ and $^2/_3$ is   .

8. Is 29 a multiple of 3?

9. $12 \times$ $= 8 \times 6$
10. If the diameter is 20 cm, what is the radius of the circle?   cm

11. $0.35 =$ %

12. $40 + y = 130$ *so* $y =$
13.

    Draw after a 270° turn clockwise.

14. If there are 10 000 Manwood fans and 1 000 Welbored football fans, what is the ratio?

15. 5 kg 720 g = $5^{720}/_{1\,000}$ = 5.

16. A triangular prism has   faces

                              edges

                              vertices

17. The angles in a triangle add up to   °.

18. The angles in a quadrilateral add up to   °.

19. Area =   m²

20. Perimeter =   m

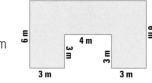

1. Is 24 a multiple of 4?

2. $6 + {}^-8 =$

3. $a - 30 = 50$ *so* $a =$

4. $^{31}/_9 =$

5. How many B boxes will fit into Box A?

6. Is 15 a composite number?

7. $6 \text{ m } 7 \text{ cm} = 6^7/_{100} \text{ cm} = 6.$

8. $a =$

9. Halve 1.2.

10. $^1/_2 > 0.07$ ☐ *true* ☐ *false*

11. $3 \quad 2 \quad 5 = 30$

12. Write $^{900}/_{1\,000}$ as a decimal.

13. Simplify $^{12}/_{30}$.

14. Round 5.496 to 2 decimal places.

15. 30, 25, 20   Rule =

16. $45 \times \quad = 10 \times 9$

17. Is 9 a prime number?

18. Draw the net of a triangular pyramid.

19. A cylinder has   faces

         edges

         vertices

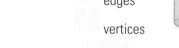

20. 2.97, 2.98, 2.99,

1. What is the perimeter of a 7-cm regular pentagon?   cm

2. What is the probability of selecting a red jelly bean from a jar with 2 red and 2 white ones?

       in

3. $5 + {}^-9 =$

4. How many faces on an octahedron?

5. $^3/_4 = 0.75$ ☐ *true* ☐ *false*

6. What is the area of a floor 6 m by 3 m?

       m^2

7. What is the perimeter?   m

8. $0.2 \times 0.6 =$

9. $50 \quad 5 \quad 2 = 5$

10. Name this triangle.

11. Tick the largest.   ☐ *4 000 000*

                   ☐ *400 000*

12. $6.07 + 12.92 =$

13. $2 \times a = 400$ *so* $a =$

14. If you draw a wall 100 mm long (scale 1:100) how long is the wall in metres?

       m

15. Which is best value for money?

   ☐ *100 g sweets at 90c*

   ☐ *150 g sweets at €1.40*

16. $1 \times \quad = 45 \div 9$

17. $2 \text{ kg } 50 \text{ g} = 2^{50}/_{100} \text{ kg} = 2. \quad$ kg

18. Is 9 a prime number?

19. Will a square and a rectangle tessellate together?

20. $^-5 + {}^-3 =$

1. $^-2 + {}^-3 =$

2. $0.6 \times 0.8 =$

3. $4 \text{ m } 5 \text{ cm} = 4^5/_{100} = 4.$ ___ m

4. 70, 140, 210, ___

5. (5 ___ 2) ___ 10 = 20

6. Which is best value for money?
   ☐ *300 g of fruit at €1.45*
   ☐ *500 g of fruit at €2.50*

7. $6 \text{ kg } 200 \text{ g} = 6^{200}/_{1\,000} \text{ kg} = 6.$ ___ kg

8. $^2/_3 + {}^2/_3 =$

9. Name this shape.

   ___

10. Add brackets to make this number sentence true.
    7 ÷ 1 − 5 + 2 = 0

11. What will I pay for a €50 jacket if there is a 20% reduction? €

12. Round 6.73 to the nearest tenth.

13. Draw the axes of symmetry on the pentagon.

14. Simplify $^{10}/_{12}$.

15. Simplify the ratio.

    10 : 5 = ___ : 1

16. Write one million and ten as a numeral.

17. Round 12.567 to 2 decimal places.

18. Write $^5/_{1\,000}$ as a decimal.

19. 12.4, 9.3, 6.2 ___ Rule =

20. What is the perimeter of a regular pentagon with 90 mm sides? ___ mm

1. $^-3 + {}^-5 =$

2. $2^5 =$

3. $40 \times y = 200$ *so* y =

4. $0.7 \times 0.4 =$

5. Change $4^3/_7$ to an improper fraction.

6. Simplify $^{15}/_{20}$.

7. (80 ___ 8) ___ 5 = 5

8. A cylinder has ___ faces ___ edges ___ vertices

9. 1, 2, 3, 5, 7, 11 ___ Rule =

10.

    How many B boxes will fit into Box A?

11. $2.543 + 3.042 =$

12. Is 64 a multiple of 8?

13. Draw as a 90° turn clockwise.

14. What is the probability of picking an odd number from a pack of cards?

    ___ in ___

15. What is the average of 5, 8, 8, 11?

16. 40% of €90.00 = €

17. $6 \times$ ___ $= 10 \times 3$

18. How many degrees make up a quadrilateral? ___°

19. The place value of 3 in 2.3 is ___.

20. Is 11 a prime number?

1. Change $^{14}/_6$ to a mixed number.

2. 20% of €80.00 = €

3. Simplify the ratio.

   20 : 5 =   : 1

4. How many degrees make up a triangle?

5. What speed is a car travelling at
   if it does 5 km every 5 minutes?   km/hr

6. ⁻4 + ⁻2 =

7. 0.9 x 0.3 =

8. A cone has   faces

                        edges

                        vertices

9. 5 m 20 cm = $5^{20}/_{100}$ cm = 5.

10. What is the average of the following numbers?
    3, 6, 7, 8

11. The meaning of 4 in 41 789?

12. Draw the net of
    a triangular prism.

13. (5   6)   20 = 10

14. Round 10.217 to 2 decimal places.

15. 10^2 =

16. What is the chance of your teacher buying you an
    ice-cream for lunch?
    (a) ☐ *certain*   (b) ☐ *very likely*   (c) ☐ *even*
    (d) ☐ *unlikely*   (e) ☐ *impossible*

17. Write $^{50}/_{1\,000}$ as a decimal.

18. Add brackets to this number sentence.
    70 ÷ 10 x 5 ÷ 1 = 35

19. 4 kg 20 g = $4^{20}/_{100}$ = 4.

20. 5.027 + 5.913 =

1. How many degrees make up a square or rectangle?
   °

2. Name this shape.

3.

   How many B boxes will fit evenly into Box A?

4. Round 8.447 to the nearest hundredth.

5. What will I pay for a €50 jacket
   if there is a 10% reduction?   €

6. Simplify the ratio.

   3 : 12 =   : 4

7. $^4/_5 + ^4/_5$ =

8. ⁻5 + ⁻4 =

9. 4.2 m =   cm

10. Write in ascending order.
    | 1.5 | 0.05 | 5 | 50 |

11. 0.5 x 0.7 =

12. 10^6 =

13. (49   7)   3 = 10

14. 1, 3, 5, 7   Rule =

15. 7 x 30 = y + 10 *so* y =

16. Which is best value for money?
    ☐ *50 g sweets at €1.15*
    ☐ *200 g sweets at €1.60*

17. 6.184 + 3.512 =

18. Is 49 a multiple of 12?

19. 4 x   = 64 ÷ 8

20. Is 13 a composite number?

1. How many degrees make up a triangle?

2. $^-7 + ^-4 =$

3. A jar has 10 red and 30 blue lollies. What is the probability of selecting a blue lolly?

   _____ in _____

4. $0.4 \times 0.4 =$

5. 5 m 40 cm $= 5^{40}/_{100} = 5.$ _____ m

6. $3^3 =$

7. 0.97, 0.98, 0.99, _____

8. Simplify $^8/_{12}$.

9. What is the average of 60, 80, 50, 90, 70?

10. 3 _____ (4 _____ 4) = 19

11. The place value of 4 in 2.004 is _____ .

12. $^7/_{10} + ^9/_{10} =$

13. A tetrahedron has _____ faces

    _____ edges

    _____ vertices

14. If a circle has a diameter of 100 cm, what is the radius? _____ cm

15. Parts of Canada are 8 hours behind GMT. If it is 5 p.m. in London, what time is it in Canada?

16. What will I pay for a €60 dress if there is a 33% reduction? _____ €

17. Simplify the ratio.

    3 : 15 = 1 : _____

18. Write a prime number between 20 and 30.

19. $^-10 + ^-6 =$

20. Round 19.567 to 2 decimal places.

1. $^-5 + ^-6 =$

2. Write in descending order.   0.015, 0.3, 0.2, 0.45.

   _____ , _____ , _____ , _____

3. Write ten million, one thousand and one as a numeral.

4. Simplify $^9/_{12}$.

5. $2^6 =$

6. 60% of €300 = € _____

7. $^7/_{10} - ^2/_{10} =$

8. $0.6 \times 0.7 =$

9. Draw the axes of symmetry on the hexagon.

10. 12 _____ (18 _____ 3) = 6

11. If there are $90 (US) to €1.00, how many euro would you get for $9.00 (US)?

12. 2 kg 5 g $= ^5/_{1\,000}$ kg = 2. _____ kg

13. If a car travels at 100 km/hr, how far can it travel in 15 minutes? _____ km

14. Name this shape.

15. a = _____

16. Simplify the ratio.

    5 : 45 = 1 : _____

17. Round 20.063 to 2 decimal places.

18. 4, 6, 8, 10, 12 _____ Rule = _____

19. $2.405 + 3.294 =$

20. Is 24 a multiple of 2 and 3?

1. Write ten million, ten thousand and ten as a numeral.

2. $^-2 + ^-3 =$

3. 10   (5   4) = 30

4. It is 8.20 p.m. in Ireland and 10.20 p.m. in Egypt. What is the time difference?

5. Write in ascending order.

   $^1/_{10}$ $^3/_4$ $^1/_2$ $^2/_{100}$

6. If there are \$90 (US) to €1.00, how many euro would you get for \$1.80 (US)?

7. Round 5.803 to 2 decimal places

8. Name this shape.

9. 31, 34, 37,   , 43

10. Write $^{450}/_{1\,000}$ as a decimal.

11. 1, 2, 3, 5, 7, 11   Rule =

12. y =

                 y°

13. 5.541 + 2.038 =

14. Is 18 a multiple of 3 and 6?

15. How many degrees make up a quadrilateral?

16. How many faces on an octahedron?

17. Are 15 and 16 composite numbers?

18. 5 000 − a = 400 x 5 *so* a =

19. What is the meaning of 9 in 973 778?

20. 0.03 =   %

1. $^-4 + ^-8 =$

2. Add brackets to this number sentence.

   80 ÷ 10 x 1 + 7 − 60 = 4

3. Name this shape.

4. 0.4 x 0.5 =

5. 8.85, 8.9, 8.95,

6. 7 m 3 cm = $7^3/_{100}$ = 7.   m

7. Draw the net of a cylinder.

8. $^8/_{20} + ^{14}/_{20} =$

9. 20   (24   2) = 8

10. Which is the best value for money?

    ☐ *€50 jacket with a 20% discount*

    ☐ *€60 jacket with a 25% discount*

11. 0.4 ≠ $^2/_5$ ☐ *true* ☐ *false*

12. 3 kg 50 g = $3^{50}/_{1\,000}$ kg = 3.   kg

13. What would I pay for a €60 dress if there is a 66% reduction?   €

14. y =

15. Simplify the ratio.

    6 : 36 = 1 :

16. Write $^{45}/_{1\,000}$ as a decimal.

17. 6.234 + 2.501 =

18. Is 12 a prime number?

19. $9^2 =$

20. If a diameter of a circle is 30 cm, what is the radius?

         cm

1. $^-4 + {}^-8 =$

2. $1.2 \times 0.3 =$

3. $6\frac{1}{2} + e = 6\frac{3}{4}$ so $e =$

4. $(2 \quad 8) \quad 4 = 12$

5. Simplify $^{200}/_{500}$.

6. Write ten million, one hundred and eleven thousand and eleven as a numeral.

7. What will I pay for a €500 bed if there is a 25% discount? €

8. Round 1.459 to the nearest tenth.

9. $y =$

10. 44, 88, 176,

11. 3 kg 40 g = $3^{40}/_{1\,000}$ kg = 3. kg

12. 70% of €300 = €

13. A sphere has ___ faces

___ edges

___ vertices

14. $(40 \div 5) \times (5 \times 10) =$

15. Double 8.9.

16. Is 13 a prime number?

17. $2.083 + 3.914 =$

18. Is 27 a multiple of 3 and 9?

19. Are 11 and 15 both prime numbers?

20. $1 = \quad\%$

1. $0.5 \times 0.8 =$

2. $20 \quad (72 \quad 9) = 12$

3. Simplify the ratio. $2 : 10 = 1 :$

4. Round 19.347 to 2 decimal places.

5. Halve 12.7.

6. 3 kg 4 g = $3^4/_{1\,000}$ kg = 3. kg

7. 3, 9, 27, 81 Rule =

8. $5.029 + 2.236 =$

9. Draw the net of a cone.

10. What is the chance of you selecting a king from a deck of playing cards?

in

11. $^-6 + {}^-4 =$

12. Are 18 and 19 both composite numbers?

13. What is the perimeter of a regular pentagon with 60-mm sides? mm

14. If a car travels 5 km in 3 minutes, how far does it travel in one hour? km

The pie chart shows the favourite sports of 6th Class pupils.

15. 32 pupils were surveyed. How many liked football?

16. How many liked cricket?

17. What percentage liked hockey?

18. What fraction liked swimming?

19. How many more liked football than cricket?

20. Write in descending order.

   2.02   2.0   2.2   2.002

WEDNESDAY

1. $^-7 + 3 =$

2. Simplify $^6/_9$.

3. 200, 20, 2,

4. (3   8)   16 = 40

5. $(700 \div 7) \div 2 =$

6. $10\,^{40}/_{50} =$ $/_{50}$ (improper fraction)

7. Double 32.5.

8. A hemisphere has   faces

                     edges

                     vertices

9. 75% of €300.00 = €

10. y =

11. A circle has a radius of 80 cm. What is the diameter?   cm

12. $2^3/_5 + e = 3^1/_5$ so e =

13. Will a circle and a triangle tessellate together?

14. What will I pay for a €500 bed if there is a 75% discount?   €

15. Write ten million, one hundred as a numeral.

16. 3 kg 400 g = $3^{400}/_{1\,000}$ kg = 3.   kg

17. 4.237 + 3.129 =

18. Write in ascending order.

     $^1/_5$ $^3/_4$ $^2/_{100}$ $^1/_3$

19. What is the perimeter of a regular hexagon with 70-mm sides?   mm

20. Which is the best value?

    ☐ €80 suit with a 75% discount

    ☐ €90 suit with a 66% discount

THURSDAY

1. $^1/_5 = 0.$

2. $^-3 + ^-5 =$

3. Draw axes of symmetry on the semicircle.

4. The place value of 5 in 2.052 is   .

5. 1.5 x 0.4 =

6. Double 17.5.

7. It is 2.15 a.m. in Ireland. It is 11.15 a.m. in Australia. What is the time difference?

8. $1^3/_5 + ^4/_5 =$

9. $6^{80}/_{100} =$ $/_{100}$ (improper fraction)

10. If there are £0.60 (UK) to €1.00, how many euro would you get for £15.00 (UK)?

11. $3^1/_5 - ^4/_5 =$

12. Simplify the ratio.   6 : 30 = 1 :

13. Round 3.654 to 2 decimal places.

14. Is 48 a multiple of 3 and 4?

15. A circular driveway has a 5 m radius. What is the diameter?   m

16. Write $^{54}/_{1\,000}$ as a decimal.

17. The meaning of 7 in 2.007 is   .

18. $8^2 =$

19. Round 6.332 to the nearest hundredth.

20. What is the perimeter of a regular octagon with 50 mm sides?   mm

1. $^-3 + ^-6 =$

2. A fridge costs €300 plus 20% VAT. What is the total price? €

3. Double the size of this shape. Draw it.

4. Convert $9\,^2/_3$ to an improper fraction.

5. $2 - 1.75 =$

6. 0.50, 0.75, _____, 1.25

7. Simplify $^{20}/_{25}$.

8. $6 \div 0.5 =$

9. Draw the axes of symmetry on this pentagon.

10. $1.5 \times 0.4 =$

11. Round 0.297 to the nearest tenth.

12. $6^3/_5 + 2^4/_5 =$

13. If a teddy bear usually costs €60.00 but is discounted by 20%, what is the new price? €

14. $6.645 - 2.032 =$

15. $6^1/_5 - {}^4/_5 =$

16. $y =$ $y°$ $120°$

17. If $^2/_3$ of a class of 30 are wearing a uniform, how many are not wearing it?

18. Are 13 and 14 both prime numbers?

19. $9.7 - e = 9$ so $e =$

20. Round 25.4371 to 3 decimal places.

1. $^-4 + ^-10 =$

2. What is the area of a path 2 m by 18 m?   m²

3. $5 \times e = 400$ so $e =$

4. Simplify $^{30}/_{35}$.

5. Write ten million, one hundred and ten thousand, one hundred and ten as a numeral.

6. $(5 \quad 8) \quad 10 = 50$

7. 6 kg 30 g $= 6^{30}/_{1\,000}$ kg = 6. _____ kg

8. If you ride your new blue bike for half an hour and cover $13^1/_2$ km, how fast are you travelling?

    km/hr

9. A square-based pyramid has _____ faces _____ edges _____ vertices

10. $2.591 + 3.273 =$

11. $^3/_5 = 0.$ _____

12. Is 21 a multiple of 6 and 7?

13. Round 15.6014 to 3 decimal places.

14. The angles in a trapezium add up to _____ °.

15.

Draw to show a 270° clockwise turn.

16. $7^2/_{10} - {}^9/_{10} =$

17. $(1\,000 \div 10) \div 5 =$

18. $6^2 =$

19. 625 mL $= {}^5/_8$ L = 0. _____ litres

20. If there are 1 000 teachers and $^3/_4$ of them are female, how many are male?

WEDNESDAY

1. The place value of 0 in 84 170 is _____ .

2. $^-6 + ^-8 =$

3. $1.3 \times 0.4 =$

4. $(100 \quad 10) \quad 4 = 6$

5. $^4/_5 = 0.$

6. $(200 \div 4) \div 10 =$

7. Halve $^1/_2$.

8. What 3-D shape can you make by stacking circles?

9. Double 13.5.

10. A cuboid has _____ faces

_____ edges

_____ vertices

11. What is the volume of the cube if its sides are 3 m?

_____ m³

12. $8.495 - 2.342 =$

13. What is the chance of selecting a €1.00 coin from a wallet consisting of €3.00 worth of €1.00 and €3.00 of 50c?

_____ in _____

14. Are 15 and 16 both composite numbers?

15. Simplify the ratio $8 : 56 = 1 :$

16. Is 33 a prime number?

17. $y =$

18. $900 \text{ mL} = {}^9/_{10} \text{ L} = 0.$ _____ litres

19. $50\% = 0.05$ ☐ *true* ☐ *false*

20. $2^4 =$

THURSDAY

1. $^1/_{10} = 0.$

2. A washing machine costs €250 plus 20% VAT. What is the total price? _____ €

3. Draw the axes of symmetry on the hexagon.

4. Double 60.5.

5. Round 2.565 to the nearest hundredth.

6. The meaning of 9 in 49 652 is _____ .

7. $1.8 \times 0.2 =$

8. $8^2/_3 + 1^2/_3 =$

9. $7 \text{ kg } 5 \text{ g} = {}^5/_{1\,000} \text{ kg} = 7.$ _____ kg

10. $x =$

11. $4.273 + 2.064 =$

12. Write in descending order.

808   1.8 $2^1/_2$

13. Is 26 a multiple of 2 and 3?

14. Round 24.0786 to 3 decimal places.

15. The angles in a parallelogram add up to _____ .

16. $25\% = 0.2$ ☐ *true* ☐ *false*

17. Write three point two four as a numeral.

18. $^{63}/_5 =$ _____ (a mixed number)

19. Simplify the ratio. $9 : 36 = 1 :$

20. It is 8.30 a.m. in Ireland. It is 3.30 a.m. in America. What is the time difference?

1. $^-6 + ^-8 =$

2. $3^3/_4 + e = 4^1/_2$ *so* e =

3. a =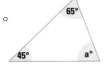

4. A DVD player costs €500 plus 20% VAT. What is the total price?

   €

5. 1.5 x 0.4 =

6. Simplify $^4/_{10}$.

7. Is 19 a prime number?

8. $30 - ^1/_3 =$

9. Draw the axes of symmetry on this hexagon.

10. $^3/_4 = 0.$

11. Write $^5/_{100}$ as a decimal. 0.

12. 8.549 − 2.035 =

13. y =

14. Round 20.4853 to 3 decimal places.

15. 750 mL = $^3/_4$ L = 0.   litres

16. 999 997, 999 998, 999 999,

17.

    Turn the rectangle 90° clockwise and draw the new position.

18. Are 17 and 21 both prime numbers?

19. 20% = 0.02   ☐ *true* ☐ *false*

20. Tick the largest.   ☐ *50% of 20*
                              ☐ *15% of 50*

1. The angles in a triangle are 40° and 85°.   °
   What is the 3rd angle?

2. 400 000, 600 000, 800 000,

3. 900 − x = 200 *so* x =

4. $10^5 =$

5. $^-4 + ^-12 =$

6. (900 ÷ 30) x 5 =

7. Halve $^1/_4$.

8. 1.6 x 0.3 =

9. If $^4/_5$ of your class of 25 eat snails for breakfast, how many do not?

10. Name this shape.

11. How many faces in the above shape?

12. How many edges?

13. How many vertices?

14. How many B boxes will fit evenly into Box A?

15. Write $^9/_{1\,000}$ as a decimal.

16. 7.569 − 5.241 =

17. (10   4)   10 = 30

18. 8 kg 250 g = $8^{250}/_{1\,000}$ kg = 8.   kg

19. Area =   m²

20. Perimeter =   m

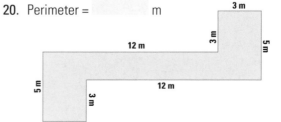

1. Double $^1/_4$.

2. A microwave costs €200 plus 20% VAT. What is the total price?

   €

3. $6 - ^2/_5 =$

4. $1.4 \times 0.5 =$

5. Round 15.5089 to 3 decimal places.

6. $1 \quad (27 \quad 3) = 10$

7. Halve $^1/_5$.

8. Name this shape.

9. How many   faces?

               edges?

               vertices?

10.

    Turn the rectangle 180° anticlockwise and draw the new position.

11. $250 \, mL = ^1/_4 \, L = 0.$ litres

12. 250 000, 500 000, 750 000,

13. Write in ascending order.

    7.07   **0.009**   **$3^1/_2$**

14. The angles in a rhombus add up to   .

15. $1^1/_4 = 1.$

16. $y =$

17. Are 100 and 150 both composite numbers?

18. A pencil case has 10 blue and 5 red pencils. What is the chance of choosing a red pencil?

             in

19. $30\% = 0.3$ ☐ *true* ☐ *false*

20. Write four point zero five as a numeral.

1. What is the perimeter of a regular octagon with 70 mm sides?

               mm

2. A truck leaves at 6.00 a.m. and arrives at its destination 6 hours later. It covers 600 km. How fast is the truck travelling?

               km/hr

3. Two angles in a triangle are 45° and 90°. What is the 3rd angle?

4. The sum of 6.4 and 0.9 is   .

5. Draw the net of a pentagonal prism.

6. Double $^1/_8$.

7. $(800 \div 40) \div 5 =$

8. $8^1/_3 + ^2/_3 =$

9. $^-8 + ^-6 =$

10. $9.541 - 2.315 =$

11. $40\% = 0.$

12. 10 000, 9 200, 8 400, 7 600,

13. Round 14.2073 to 3 decimal places.

14. $5 \, kg \, 4 \, g = 5^4/_{1\,000} \, kg = 5.$

15. Write in descending order.

    $^1/_2$ **0.049**   **0.1**   **3%**

16. 400 is a composite number.   ☐ *true* ☐ *false*

17. Write $^{11}/_{1\,000}$ as a decimal. 0.

18. The angles in a kite add up to   .

19. Tick the largest.   ☐ *75% of 40*

                      ☐ *35% of 100*

20. Are all the angles in an equilateral triangle acute?

1. If the diameter of a circle is 300 cm, what is the radius? _____ cm

2. $900 - e = 500$ so $e =$

3. Draw the axes of symmetry on this hexagon.

4. $^-4 + ^-9 =$

5. Write in descending order.

   5%   0.9   0.11   0.222

6. Simplify $^{16}/_{20}$.

7. $1.8 \times 0.3 =$

8. $9.638 - 4.374 =$

9. Round 16.6324 to 3 decimal places.

10. Tick the largest.   ☐ *25% of 80*
    ☐ *30% of 100*

11. 0.8, 1.1, 1.4, 1.7, _____

12. 25% of €100.00 = € _____

13. The total cost of 5 sweets is 70c. What is the average cost of a sweet? _____ c

14. The meaning of 7 in 47 096 is _____.

15. $4^3 =$

16. If there are £0.60 (UK) to €1.00, how many euro for £30.00 (UK)?

17. Write the co-ordinates of point A.

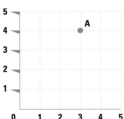

18. (3 ___ 5) ___ 5 = 20

19. Write ten million, nine hundred and ninety thousand and ninety.

20. $3a + 10 = 19$ so $a =$

1. $^-2 + ^-9 =$

2. A fridge costs €250 plus 20% VAT. What is the total price? _____ €

3. $(240 \div 60) \times 7 =$

4. $1.5 \times 0.5 =$

5. Two angles in a triangle are 90° and 40°. What is the 3rd angle? _____ °

6. 2 500, 2 250, 2 000, _____

7. Draw the axes of symmetry on this octagon.

8. Round 14.3692 to 3 decimal places.

9. How many faces on a triangular prism?

10. 500 mL = $^1/_2$ L = 0. _____ litres

11. 30% = 0.3   ☐ *true* ☐ *false*

12. $32 = 2^a$ so $a =$

13. What is the chance of throwing a 6 on a dice? _____ in _____

14. A pentagonal prism has _____ faces

    _____ edges

    _____ vertices

15. $4y - 10 = 10$ so $y =$

16. Write the co-ordinates of point A.

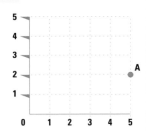

17. Area = _____ m²

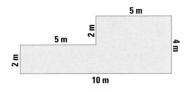

18. Perimeter = _____ m

19. 10 ___ (8 ___ 4) = 12

20. How many right angles in a square?

1. Draw the net of a cylinder.

2. $^-3 + {}^-6 =$

3. $4^3 =$

4. $7.849 + 2.591 =$

5. Are 23 and 25 both prime numbers?

6. $75\% = 0.7$ ☐ *true* ☐ *false*

7. The total cost of 4 chocolate bars is 80c. What is the average cost of a chocolate bar?

8. $y =$

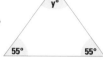

9. $6 \text{ kg } 24 \text{ g} = 6^{24}/_{1\,000} = 6.$ _____ kg

10. Write in ascending order. $4\%, 6^1/_4, 0.5, 2$

    _____ , _____ , _____ ,

11. $23 + e = 30$ *so* $e =$

12. What is the chance of tossing a coin and it landing on a 'head'?

    _____ in _____

13. $^{12}/_{20} = 0.$

14. Write $^{40}/_{100}$ as a decimal.

15. $10 - 0.9 =$

16. $2a - 15 = 25$ so $a =$

17. $y =$

18. The meaning of 4 in 45 226 is _____ .

19. How many right angles in a trapezium?

20. 20 _____ $(64$ _____ $8) = 12$

1. What is the size of this angle? _____ °

2. A car costs €10 000 plus 20% VAT. What is the total price? €

3. $1.3 \times 0.6 =$

4. $6.537 - 2.184 =$

5. 40% of €500 = €

6. $7^2 =$

7. Round 23.0679 to 3 decimal places.

8. Simplify $^{18}/_{21}$.

9. $(320 \div 80) \times 9 =$

10.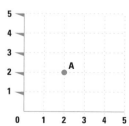

    Draw the rectangle after a 450° turn anticlockwise.

11. $400 \text{ mL} = {}^2/_5 \text{ L} = 0.$ _____ litres

12. Are 16 and 18 both composite numbers?

13. $8 - 0.02 =$

14. Tick the largest. ☐ *75% of 60*
    ☐ *80% of 50*

15. Can a triangle and a square tessellate together?

16. $0.05 =$ _____ %

17. Two angles in a triangle are 85° and 45°. What is the 3rd angle? _____ °

18. $5a - 15 = 15$ so $a =$

19. Write the co-ordinates of point A.

20. If you are paid €5.00 an hour for cleaning your room (it takes 3 hours!), how much do you earn?

    €

1. How many right angles in a rectangle?

2. What is the perimeter of a regular pentagon with 40-mm sides? _____ mm

3. $^-9 + {}^+3 =$

4. Write $10^3/_8$ as an improper fraction.

5. 350, 700, 1 050, 1 400, 1 750, _____

6. 9 000 − e = 6 000 *so* e =

7. 1.5 x 0.2 =

8. Round 12.5675 to 3 decimal places.

9. What is the chance of being born on a Monday? ____ in ____

10. What is the average of these cricket scores? 4, 0, 35

11. 1% = 0.

12. The value of 5 in 250 470 =

13. Write the co-ordinates of point A.

14. Write the co-ordinates of point B.

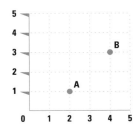

15. 5 ____ (40 ____ 2) = 25

16. If there are £0.60 (UK) to €1.00, how many euro for £6.00 (UK)?

17. Draw to show a 270° turn anticlockwise.

18. A car costs €5 000 plus 20% VAT. What is the total price? €

19. Two angles in a triangle are 75° and 60°. What is the 3rd angle? °

20. If you are paid $1^1/_2$ times the normal rate (€5.00 per hour) what do you earn for 2 hours work?

€

1. $^-10 + {}^+7 =$

2. 9.527 − 6.285 =

3. Write ten million, one thousand and one as a numeral.

4. Tick the largest: ☐ *75% of 80*
   ☐ *70% of 90*

5. $2^e = 32$ *so* e =

6. Write in ascending order.

   99 080   **41 700**   **69 022**

7. The total cost of four pens is 48c. What is the average cost of a pen? c

8. Name this triangle.

9. 5% = 0.

10. 5a − 5 = 20 so a =

11. The angles in a triangle are 80° and 60°. What is the 3rd angle? °

12. 300 g = 0.

13. y =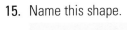

14. Draw the net of a cube.

15. Name this shape.

16. (600 ÷ 30) x 50 =

17. 250 mL = $^1/_4$ L = 0. _____ litres

18. $5^3 =$

19. Write two million, twenty thousand and two as a numeral.

20. 75% = $^3/_4$ = 0.

WEDNESDAY

1. 1.7 x 0.3 =

2. Halve 0.04.

3. $^8/_{20}$ = 0.

4. 40 x 70 = e + 800 *so* e =

5. Round 15.23 to 1 decimal place.

6. The value of 6 in 650 450 is

7. $^2/_3$ of 30 =

8. x =

9. 4% = 0.

10. 30   (4   6) = 6

11. What is the average of these cricket scores?
25, 50, 60, 75

12. y =

13. Double 12.6.

14. 10a − 3 = 27 so a =

15. 200 mL = $^1/_5$ L = 0.   litres

16. You clean your room on Sunday and your mum pays you double time (normal rate 35c per hour). How much did you earn after 3 hours?

    €

17. What is the lowest common denominator for $^3/_{25}$ and $^2/_5$?

18. 20% = $^1/_5$ = 0.

19. Write in descending order.

    $^1/_4$ 8%   0.1

20. How many right angles in a parallelogram?

THURSDAY

1. 8.319 − 4.163 =

2. If $^2/_3$ of your teachers ride a bicycle to school, what fraction do not ride to school?

3. Name this triangle.

4. $^4/_5$ of 50 =

5. 1 000 000, 10 000, 100,

6. Halve 0.08.

7. 289 kg = 0.   t

8. $^-5 + {^+}8$ =

9. Tick the largest: ☐ *75% of 80*
                      ☐ *70% of 90*

10. Write the co-ordinates of point A.

11. Write the co-ordinates of point B.

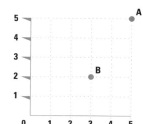

12. Double 14.6.

13. 400 mm = 0.   m

14. What is the LCD for $^3/_{25}$ and $^4/_{10}$?

15. $^2/_{25}$ = 0.

16. 6a − 4 = 20 so a =

17. What is the floor area of a classroom 9 m by 6 m?

    m^2

18. 11^2 =

19. A car costs €2 500 plus 20% VAT. What is the total price?

    €

20. 30% = $^3/_{10}$ = 0.

1. $^-4 + ^+5 =$

2. $1.8 \times 0.2 =$

3. Round 3.4672 to 3 decimal places.

4. Write $^{64}/_9$ as a mixed number.

5. 5 000, 4 000, 3 000,

6. 60% discount on a €20.00 item.

   New price = €

7. $2\,000 = 400 + y$ *so* $y =$

8. Cara is travelling at 60 km per hour. How long will it take to travel 1 km? ____ min

9. The place value of 7 in 74 012 is ____.

10. 65 mL = 0.____ L

11. Double 8.09.

12. Halve 8.09.

13. $2^1/_2 =$ ____ %

14. What is the volume of a box 20 cm by 30 cm by 40 cm?

    ____ cm^3

15. (6 ____ 5) ____ 10 = 20

16. If there are $0.90 (US) to €1.00, how many euro for $2.70? (US)?

17.

    Draw to show a 180° turn.

18. What is the average of these class results?
    85%   **60%**   **35%**

19. Two angles in a triangle are 70° and 80°. ____ °
    What is the 3rd angle?

20. Tick the largest: ☐ *20% of 100*
                        ☐ *50% of 50*

1. $^-5 + ^+2 =$

2. What is the LCD for $^2/_3$ and $^6/_8$?

3. The place value of 6 in 46 707.

4. $(40 \div 8) \times (8 - 5) =$

5. $1\,200 - a = 700$ *so* $a =$

6. 30% discount on a €300.00 item.

   New price = €

7. Double 7.009.

8. Name this triangle.

9. A car costs €7 500 plus 20% VAT. What is the total price?   €

10. How many lines of symmetry does this letter have?

11. 89 m = 0.____ km

12. $4^3/_4 =$ ____ (improper fraction)

13. How many right angles in a square?

The pie chart shows the number of events won by each team at sports day.

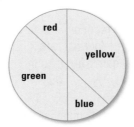

14. There were 32 events in total. How many events did the yellow team win?

15. What fraction of events did the green team win?

16. How many events did the red team win?

17. What fraction of events did the blue team win?

18. Did the red and blue teams win the same amount of events?

19. $^-3 + ^+9 =$

20. $1.7 \times 0.3 =$

1. Double 16.008.
2. Write another name for a 3-D shape that is a tetrahedron.
3. $9\frac{1}{3} - e = 8\frac{2}{3}$ so e =
4. $^-6 + {}^+2 =$
5. What is the LCD for $\frac{3}{4}$ and $\frac{2}{10}$?
6. Round 20.0756 to 3 decimal places.
7. The place value of 8 in 24 850.
8. y =
9. If you ride 8 km in a quarter of an hour, how far can you ride in 2 hours?   km
10. Tick the largest: ☐ *10% of 50*
    ☐ *40% of 25*
11. $9.5\% = 0.$
12. The total cost of 3 pens is 48c. What is the average cost of a pen?   c
13. $5y + 10 = 20$ so y =
14. $600 \text{ mL} = \frac{3}{5} = 0.$
15. $10\% = \frac{1}{10} = 0.$
16. Show a 90° turn anticlockwise.
17. Round 0.087 to the nearest hundredth.
18. Write the co-ordinates of point A.
19. Write the co-ordinates of point B.

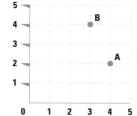

20. $13 \text{ cm} = 0.$ m

1. $1.5 \times 0.6 =$
2. What is the chance of choosing a face card from a deck of playing cards?   in
3. Ben is travelling at 60 km per hour. How long will it take to travel 5 km?   mins.
4. What is the area of a wall 7 m by 4 m?   m²
5. A circle with a 9 m radius has a diameter of   m.
6. Halve 0.03.
7. $5\frac{2}{20} - \frac{15}{20} =$
8. $(30 \qquad 2) \qquad 5 = 20$
9. The angles in a triangle are 95° and 50°. What is the 3rd angle?   °
10. The total cost of 5 stickers is 90c. What is the average cost of a sticker?   c
11. How many degrees make up a square?   °
12. $45 \div 5 = 3 \times a$ so a =
13. Round 7.097 to the nearest tenth.
14. Show a 90° turn anticlockwise.
15.

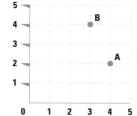

The area of the house is 200 m². What is the area of the garden?   m²
16. The perimeter of the house is 60 m. What is the perimeter of the garden?   m
17. $3.5\% = 0.$
18. $6y - 10 = 20$ so y =
19. $60\% = \frac{3}{5} = 0.$
20. Draw a vertical line.

MONDAY

1. Mary earns €300. She gets a 5% payrise. What will her new wage be?

   €

2. $^-9 + ^+3 =$

3. What do we call an angle that is 90°?

4. The meaning of 5 in 7.095.

5. $1.0 - 0.075 =$

6. $1.5 \times 0.4 =$

7. Simplify $^{30}/_{60}$.

8. $10 \times a = 5\,000$ *so* $a =$

9. Betty is travelling at 30 km per hour. How long will it take her to travel 10 km?

   minutes

10. Write in ascending order.

    0.99　　　$3^2/_3$　　　**5%**

11. 3 500, 7 000, 10 500,

12. The total cost of 5 pens is 95c. What is the average cost of a pen? c

13. How many vertices on a sphere?

14. $3.2\% = 0.$

15. $875 \text{ mL} = {}^7/_8 \text{ L} = 0.$ litres

16. 10% off a €200.00 item = €

17. $12.5\% = {}^1/_8 = 0.$

18. 2.5 m by 1 m? m²

19. What number is half way between −4 and +6?

20. $2 \text{ g} = 0.$ kg

TUESDAY

1. If there are $0.90 (US) to €1.00, how many euro for $18.00 (US)?

2. $^-10 + ^+4 =$

3. $18 \div 0.5 =$

4. 650, 1 050, 1 450, 1 850,

5. Double 27.06.

6. $60 \times a = 3\,000$ *so* $a =$

7. What do we call an angle that is between 0° and 90°?

8. Jade earns €400. She gets a 2% pay rise. What will her new wage be?

   €

9. Name this shape.

10. $1.6 \times 0.3 =$

11. $4.9\% = 0.$

12. Round 27.0359 to 3 decimal places.

13. The place value of 8 in 38 071 is .

14. A car costs €1 250 plus 20% VAT. What is the total price? €

15. $4y + 4 = 20$ *so* $y =$

16. $33\% = {}^1/_3 = 0.$

17. What is the next square number after 36?

18. $10^2 =$

19. Which digit in the decimal 8.75 is the tenth?

20. How many edges on a cylinder?

1. Write the co-ordinates of point A.

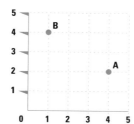

2. Write the co-ordinates of point B.

3. $^-5 + {^+}9 =$

4. What do we call an angle that is between 90° and 180°?

5. $^5/_{20} > {^1}/_2$ ☐ true ☐ false

6. A car costs €1 500 plus 20% VAT. What is the total price?   €

7. Double $^1/_4$.

8. The total cost of 4 sweets is 84c. What is the average cost of a sweet?   c

9. $9.3 - a = 8.9$ *so* $a =$

10. $6y + 2 = 20$ *so* $y =$

11. $700\ mL = {^7}/_{10}\ L = 0.$ litres

12. A jam factory loses $^1/_{10}$ of its 1 000 jars due to breakage. How many are lost?

13. Name this shape.

14. What number is half way between −2 and +8?

15. Which digit in the decimal 8.75 is in the hundredths?

16. Write the fractions from smallest to largest.

$^3/_4$ $^1/_2$ $^1/_8$ $^5/_8$

17. $150\ kg = 0.$ t

18. The angles in a rhombus add up to   °.

19. What is the chance of a tossed coin landing on a 'tail'?   in

20. What is the number after 999 999?

1. $1.8 \times 0.2 =$

2. David earns €300. He gets a 3% pay rise. What will his new wage be?

€

3. $y =$

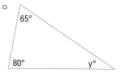

4. $40 \times a =$ half of 400 *so* $a =$

5. Simplify $^{50}/_{100}$.

6. Double $15^1/_2$.

7. Round 15.5481 to 3 decimal places.

8. Sarah is travelling at 30 km per hour. How long will it take to travel 1 km?   mins.

9. The place value of 4 in 425 000 is   .

10. $y =$

11. $9y - 2 = 70$ *so* $y =$

12. $40\% = {^2}/_5 = 0.$

13. 2.8, 3.1, 3.4, 3.7,

14. What is the next square number after 81?

15. $6^1/_3 \neq 6.3$ ☐ true ☐ false

16. The angles in a parallelogram add up to   °.

17. What is the chance of a dice landing on an odd number?   in

18. $7\ mm = 0.$ m

19. Write the fractions from smallest to largest.

$^2/_3$ $^3/_6$ $^1/_3$ $^8/_9$

20. How many faces on a hemisphere?

MONDAY

1. $0.5 \div 0.25 =$

2. $^-4 + {^+7} =$

3. Vanessa earns €500. She gets a 2% pay rise. What is her new wage? €

4. $a + 11.7 = 12.5$ *so* $a =$

5. 500, 450, 400,

6. $(200 \div 2) \times (50 - 45) =$

7. $1.1\% = 0.$

8. The total cost of 6 pencils is €1.50. What is the average cost of a pencil?   c

9. $800 \text{ mL} = {^4/_5} \text{L} = 0.$ litre

10. 25% off a €400.00 item is a saving of …   €   .

11. What number is halfway between −5 and +5?

12. Write ten million, eight hundred as a numeral.

13. A television costs €400 plus 20% VAT. What is the total price?   €

14. Which digit in the decimal 8.125 is the hundredth?

15. A blue circle has a radius of 270 cm.

    Its diameter is   cm.

16. $45 \text{ mL} = 0.$ L

17. If a painter charged €3.00 per square metre to paint a 7 m x 2 m wall, it cost

    €   .

18. How many faces on an octahedron?

19. The area of a house is 1 000 m². What is the area of the garden?

              m²

20. The perimeter of the house is 130 m. What is the perimeter of the garden?

              m

[Diagram: garden 50 m wide, house 40 m wide, 50 m and 25 m heights labelled, "garden" and "house"]

TUESDAY

1. Is N symmetrical?   ☐ *yes* ☐ *no*

2. An octahedron has: faces
                               edges
                               vertices

3. $y + 1\,200 = 3\,000$ *so* $y =$

4. $0.75 \div 0.25 =$

5. $^-5 + {^+3} =$

6. Double 0.65.

7. $9\,000 - a = 5\,500$ *so* $a =$

8. Draw as a 90° turn clockwise.

9. What do we call an angle that is 90°?

10. $^1/_2 < {^1/_5}$ ☐ *true* ☐ *false*

11. Kate is travelling at 60 km per hour. How long will it take her to travel 10 km?

              minutes

12. $25\% = {^1/_4} = 0.$

13. $3y + 4 = 28$ *so* $y =$

14. What is the next square number after 9?

15. What is the chance of selecting a girls' name from a hat if there are 15 girls' names and 5 boys' names?

              in

16. $110 \text{ m} = 0.$ km

17. Write the co-ordinates of point A.

18. Write the co-ordinates of point B.

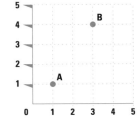

19. What is the perimeter of a regular hexagon with 30-mm sides?   mm

20. Which digit in the decimal 8.125 is the thousandth?

WEDNESDAY

1. $0.8 \div 0.2 =$

2. $4 \text{ cm} = 0.$ m

3. Double 0.95.

4. Are either of the letters S or E symmetrical?

5. $y =$

6. $^-9 + {}^+6 =$

7. Ben earns €400. He gets a 4% pay rise. What is his new wage?   €

8. What do we call an angle between 0° and 90°?

9. $660 \text{ mL} = {}^2/_3 \text{ L} = 0.$ litres

10. Name this shape.

11. 0.2, 0.6, 1, 1.4,

12. How many lines of symmetry has the letter E?

13. $^1/_3$ of $y = 9$ *so* $y =$

14. $40\% = {}^4/_{10} = 0.$

15. If there are $0.90 (US) to €1.00, how many euro for $6.30 (US)?

16. A computer costs €800 plus 20% VAT. What is the total price?

     €

17. $4.4\% = 0.$

18. $100 - e = 60$ *so* $e =$

19. Write the fractions from smallest to largest.

    $^6/_8$ $^1/_8$ $^5/_{10}$ $^1/_4$

20. How many edges on a tetrahedron?

THURSDAY

1. What is the area of a floor 12 m by 11 m?

     m²

2. $0.9 \div 0.3 =$

3. What do we call the angle between 90° and 180°?

4. Simon is travelling at 30 km per hour. How long will it take him to travel 5 km?

     minutes

5. $1 \text{ kg} = 0.$ t

6. The total cost of 7 pens is €1.54. What is the average cost of a pen?   c

7. $80\% = {}^4/_5 = 0.$

8. $10^4/_{10} - {}^6/_{10} =$

9. Double 0.55.

10. $y =$

11. Is 500 a prime number?

12. What number is halfway between −8 and +4?

13. 4, 12, 20, 28,

14. How many B boxes will fit evenly into Box A?

15. Round 10.056 to the nearest tenth.

16. Which digit in the decimal 8.125 is the tenth?

17. Draw the net of a triangular prism.

18. Halve $12^1/_2$.

19. Write the fractions from smallest to largest.

    $^1/_2$ $^2/_3$ $^2/_6$ $^7/_9$

20. How many vertices on a cube?

1. $0.6 \div 0.2 =$

2. $0.96, 0.97, 0.98, 0.99,$

3. What would be the perimeter of a regular hexagon with 60-mm sides? _____ mm

4. $^{-}7 + {}^{+}3 =$

5. The total price of four pizzas is €24. What is the average cost of a pizza? € _____

6. $\frac{1}{2} < \frac{1}{10}$ ☐ *true* ☐ *false*

7. 8 L 253 mL = $8^{253}/_{100}$ L = 8. _____ litres

8. $7 - 0.04 =$

9. Which digit in the decimal 4.705 is the thousandth?

10. $20\% = {}^{2}/_{10} = 0.$

11. Is the formulae: **area = l + w** correct?

12. $5^2 =$

13. A cube has 2-cm by 2-cm faces. What is the cube's surface area? _____ cm³

14. Write three capital letters that are symmetrical.

15. $6\% = 0.$

16. Round 3.06 (nearest tenth).

17.

Spin the triangle 450° anticlockwise. Draw its new position.

18.
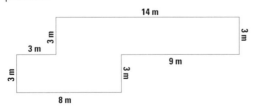

Area = _____ m²

19. Perimeter = _____ m

20. Tick which would be best to measure the width of a book.

☐ *ruler* ☐ *trundle wheel* ☐ *metre stick*

1. $^{3}/_{4} > {}^{1}/_{2}$ ☐ *true* ☐ *false*

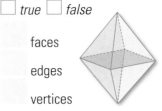

2. An octahedron has: _____ faces

_____ edges

_____ vertices

3. $0.9 \div 0.3 =$

4. $^{-}4 + {}^{+}9 =$

5. $75\ 000, 150\ 000, 225\ 000,$

6. 5 L 450 mL = $5^{450}/_{1\ 000}$ L = 5. _____ litre

7. What do we call an angle that is 90°?

8. What is the perimeter? _____ mm

9. $66\% = {}^{2}/_{3} = 0.$

10. Name this shape.

11. $6^2 =$

12. Is the formulae: **area = l – w** correct?

13. Will a hexagon and a square tessellate together?

14. A cube has 3-cm by 3-cm faces. What is the cube's surface area? _____ cm³

15. Draw the axes of symmetry on the irregular pentagon.

16. Round 6.14 (nearest tenth).

17. Tick which would be best to measure the height of your teacher.

☐ *ruler* ☐ *trundle wheel* ☐ *metre stick*

18. $9\% = 0.$

19. The place value of 9 in 952 075 is

_____.

20. Are 18 and 81 both composite numbers?

WEDNESDAY

1. $0.75 \div 0.25 =$
2. Write the co-ordinates of point A.
3. Write the co-ordinates of point B.

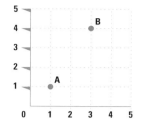

4. 1.07, 1.08, 1.09,

5. What is the perimeter?   cm
6. $8^2 =$
7. What do we call an angle that is between 0° and 90°?
8. $37.5\% = {}^3/_8 = 0.$
9. Round 4.378 (nearest tenth).
10. A cube has 4-cm by 4-cm faces. What is the cube's surface area? cm^3
11. $110\% =$ (decimal)

The graph shows the number of sunny days for the first six months of a year.

12. Which month had 13 sunny days?
13. Which month had the most sunny days?
14. Which month had the least sunny days?
15. How many more sunny days had March than January?
16. Which month had fewer sunny days than you might expect?
17. Which month had 23 sunny days?
18. Which month would have the greatest chance of sunny days if you went for a picnic?
19. Tick which would be best to measure the length of your foot.
    ☐ *ruler*   ☐ *trundle wheel*   ☐ *metre stick*
20. Which digit in the decimal 4.705 is the tenth?

THURSDAY

1. $^-5 + {}^+3 =$
2. The total cost of 5 drinks is €6.25. What is the average cost of a drink? €
3.

   Turn this rectangle 90° clockwise and draw the new position.
4. $0.9 \div 0.15 =$
5. 50, 5, 100, 10, 200,
6. $7 \text{ L } 945 \text{ mL} = 7{}^{945}/_{1\,000} \text{ L} = 7.$ litres
7. Which digit in the decimal 4.705 is the hundredth?
8. $11^2 =$
9. $5.5 - 0.9 =$
10. What is the perimeter?

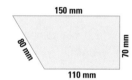

                    mm
11. ${}^3/_5 < {}^1/_2$ ☐ *true* ☐ *false*
12. What do we call an angle that is between 90° and 180°?
13. What is the probability of choosing a head on a one coin toss?

                    in
14. $80\% = {}^8/_{10} = 0.$
15. Is the formulae: **Area = L x W** correct?
16. $1 =$ %
17. A cube has 5-cm by 5-cm faces. What is the cube's surface area? cm^3
18. Round 2.056 (nearest tenth).
19. How many degrees make up a square?
20. Will a parallelogram and an isosceles triangle tessellate together?

1. What do we call an angle that is between 180° and 360°?

2. $2^5 =$

3. $0.6 \div 0.15 =$

4. $6^1/_4 =$ _____ (improper fraction)

5. Write ten million, five hundred and twelve thousand and fifteen as a numeral.

6. 8% of €10.00 = €

7. What is the place value of 4 in 2.4 million?

8. The total cost of 6 drinks is €7.20. What is the average cost of a drink? €

9. What is the angle between the hands on an analogue clock displaying 9 o'clock?

   °

10. Which is a composite number?
    ☐ 15   ☐ 11

11. 80 x 30 = 24 x y *so* y =

12. $4/_5 + 2^4/_5 =$

13.

    Draw to show a 270° turn clockwise.

14. Round 15.6073 to 3 decimal places.

15. Write the formulae to work out an area:

    a = _____ **x** _____

16. Change $2^4/_7$ to an improper fraction.

17. Tick which scales would be best to weigh a banana.
    ☐ *kitchen scales*   ☐ *bathroom scales*

18. What is the volume of a box 40 cm by 30 cm by 40 cm?

    _____ cm³

19. $0.7 < 8/_{10}$ ☐ *true* ☐ *false*

20. If there are ¥116 to €1.00, how many euro would you get for ¥580?

1. Simplify $18/_{24}$.

2. Write 3.65 million as a numeral.

3. How much are the wages if you pay time and a half for 4 hours (normal rate €10.00 per hour)?

   €

4. $7^3/_4 =$ _____ . (decimal)

5. What do we call an angle that is 90°?

6. 6.05 km = _____ m

7. $^-7 + {}^+3 =$

8. 9 L 45 mL = $9^{45}/_{1\,000}$ L = 9.

9. Tick which would be best to measure the length of the street:
   ☐ *ruler*   ☐ *trundle wheel*   ☐ *metre stick*

10. How far do you go in an hour if you take 5 minutes to go 6 km? _____ km

11. Which digit in the decimal 0.527 is the tenth?

12. Write $49/_6$ as a mixed number.

13. Round 21.3689 to 3 decimal places.

14. What is the diameter of a circular driveway with a 10 m radius? _____ m

15. A shape has six 2-cm by 3-cm faces. What is the shape's surface area? _____ cm³

16. What is the average of these cricket scores? 8, 15, 8, 15, 0

17. $5\,000 \div (50 \times 10^2) =$

18. Are 210 and 120 both prime numbers?

19. $3.3 > 3^1/_5$ ☐ *true* ☐ *false*

20. Tick which scales would be best to weigh a dog.
    ☐ *kitchen scales*   ☐ *bathroom scales*

WEDNESDAY

1. If there are ¥116 to €1.00, how many euro would you get for ¥232?

2. Write 8.2 million as a numeral.

3. Simplify $^{15}/_{18}$.

4. 7.092 L =   mL

5. What speed are you travelling if your bike does 1 km in 4 minutes?   km/hr

6. $9^4/_5$ =   (improper fraction)

7. 0.9 ÷ 0.3 =

8. $^-5 + {}^+9$ =

9. The total cost of 8 cakes is €4.40. What is the average cost of a cake?   c

10. Draw a net of a cube.

11. Change $5^3/_8$ to an improper fraction.

12. Tick which would be best to measure the height of a door.

   ☐ *ruler*   ☐ *trundle wheel*   ☐ *metre stick*

13. Which digit in the decimal 5.026 is the thousandth?

14. 87.5% + $^7/_8$ = 0.

15. 4 x y = 280 *so* y =

16. Write the formulae to work out an area:

   a = l   w

17. A shape has six 2-cm by 4-cm faces. What is the shape's surface area?   cm³

18. Write in ascending order.

   1%   **0.1**   **$^5/_{10}$**   **0.99**

19. Draw a dot at co-ordinate (2,3) and label it 'A'.

20. Draw a dot at co-ordinate (5,4) and label it 'B'.

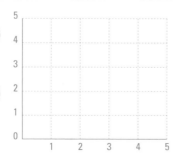

THURSDAY

1. What is the probability of being born on a Sunday?

     in

2. $^-15 + {}^-2$ =

3. What do we call an angle that is between 0° and 90°?

4. 10 L 8 mL = $10^8/_{1\,000}$ L = 10.

5. Which digit is the decimal 5.234 is the hundredth?

6. 62.5% = $^5/_8$ = 0.

7. Write five million and five as a numeral.

8. Halve 8.5.

9. 1 800, 2 600, 3 400,

10. Draw the net of a cylinder.

11. What is the ratio of boys to girls if there are 8 boys and 24 girls?

12. 6 030 mm =   m

13. 6.9 − 1.1 =

14. y =

15. Round 12.5467 to 3 decimal places.

16. Tick which scales would be best to weigh an apple.

   ☐ *kitchen scales*   ☐ *bathroom scales*

17. 85 000, 100 000, 115 000,

18. The area of the house is 400 m². What is the area of the garden?

     m²

19. The perimeter of the house is 80 m. What is the perimeter of the garden?

     m

20. 1.5 ÷ 0.3 =

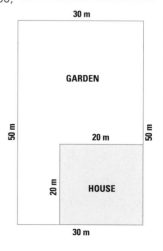

1. Write 1.3 million as a numeral.

2. $2.1 \div 0.7 =$

3. If you enlarge this line ├───┤ by 4:1 the new line will equal _____ cm.

4. Is the formulae: **diameter = 2 x r** correct?

5. Tick which scales would be best to weigh a potato.
   ☐ *kitchen scales*   ☐ *bathroom scales*

6. $5 \text{ L } 4 \text{ mL} = 5^4/_{1\,000} = 5.$ _____ litres

7. $^1/_2 \text{ x } ^1/_4 =$

8. $9^2 =$

9. The chance of me turning into a fish is
   ☐ 0%   ☐ 50%   ☐ 100%

10. What is the average shoe size? 4, 10, 13

11. $10^5 =$

12. Draw a dot at co-ordinate (5,3) and label 'A'.

13. Draw a dot at co-ordinate (1,4) and label 'B'.

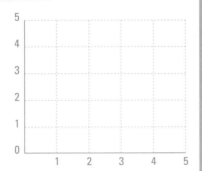

14. $a + 2.3 = 3.1$ *so* $a =$

15. A shape has six 3-cm by 3-cm faces. What is the shape's surface area? _____ cm³

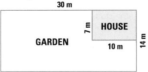

16. The area of the house is 70 m². What is the area of the garden? _____ m²

17. The perimeter of the house is 34 m. What is the perimeter of the garden? _____ m

18. There are 0.6 euro to 1 Canadian dollar. How many euro would you exchange for 20 Canadian dollars?

19. Write the numeral fifteen point zero four.

20. $7.205 \text{ kg} =$ _____ g

1. If there are ¥116 to €1.00, how many euro would you get for ¥1 160?

2. What is the floor area of a kitchen 10 m by 3.5 m? _____ m²

3. An octahedron has: ☐ *faces*
   ☐ *edges*
   ☐ *vertices*

4. Write 6.09 million as a numeral.

5. 63 000, 71 000, 79 000, _____

6. Round 14.9721 to 3 decimal places.

7. $2.5 \div 0.5 =$

8. What is the average of these ages? 15, 21, 23, 19, 27

9. Rotate 540° clockwise.

10. Tick which would be best to measure the perimeter of a field.
    ☐ *ruler*   ☐ *trundle wheel*   ☐ *metre stick*

11. $^1/_2 \text{ x } ^1/_2 =$

12. The chance of me tossing a 'tail' on a coin is
    ☐ 0%   ☐ 50%   ☐ 100%

13. What is your pay if you work 3 hours of overtime at time and a half (normal rate is €10.00 per hour)?
    € _____

14. A shape has six 4-cm by 2-cm faces. What is the shape's surface area? _____ cm³

15. What is the probability of your name being picked out of a hat in your class? _____ in _____

16. $80\,000 = 8 \text{ x } 10y$ *so* $y =$

17. $6^1/_4 - ^3/_4 =$

18. There are 6 euro to 10 Australian dollars. How many euro would you exchange for 50 Australian dollars?

19. $1.07 \text{ m} =$ _____ cm

20. Order the fractions from smallest to largest.
    $^7/_8$ $^1/_4$ $^3/_4$ $^1/_2$

1. Write 2.75 million as a numeral.

2. Round 21.5875 to 3 decimal places.
3. What is the average of these shoe sizes? 4, 7, 5, 3, 6

4. $^3/_4$, 1, $1^1/_2$, $2^1/_4$, $3^1/_4$,
5. What is the length of this line ⊢ if it is lengthened by 3:1?
6. The time is 2.30 p.m. in Ireland and 9.30 a.m. in New York. What is the time difference?

7. Is the formulae: **diameter = 4 x r** correct?
8. Tick which scales would be best to weigh a bag of sugar.

    ☐ *kitchen scales* ☐ *bathroom scales*

9. $^1/_4$ x $^1/_2$ =
10. A shape has six 1-cm by 6-cm faces. What is the shape's surface area? cm³
11. Write the prime numbers from 10 to 20.

    ,   ,   and

12. What should you earn if you received double time for 6 hours of work? (Normal rate €10.00 per hour.)

    €

13. 4^2 and 5^2 =

14. 8.005 m = mm
15. $2^1/_2$ > 2.055 ☐ *true* ☐ *false*

The graph shows the average height of children aged 8–12 at St Mary's Primary school.

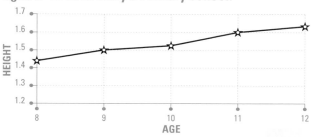

16. Which age has an average height of 1.5 m?

17. Which age has the tallest children?
18. How much taller are 11 year olds than 9 year olds?
19. Which age has shorter children than you might expect?
20. Which age has an average height of 1.44 m?

1. What is the perimeter of a square with 9-cm sides?

    cm

2. 2.4 ÷ 4 =
3. Tick which scales would be best to weigh a man.
    ☐ *kitchen*   ☐ *bathroom*
4. Write 3.05 million as a numeral.

5. 3 L 55 mL = $3^{55}/_{1\,000}$ L = 3. litres

6. $^3/_4$ x $^1/_2$ =

7. What is the average? 2, 4, 5, 6, 8

8. 15 000, 95 000, 175 000,

9. The chance of me eating today is:
    ☐ 0% ☐ 50% ☐ 100%

10. There are 7 euro to 1 000 Japanese yen. How many euro would you exchange for 5 000 Japanese yen?

11. 3.75 + 0.25 =

12. Round 12.5437 to 3 decimal places.

13. 10^6 =

14. What do you call an angle that is between 180° and 360°?

15. $^1/_5$ of an hour = minutes
16. Is the formulae: **diameter = 3 x r** correct?

17. $7^1/_4$ < 7.3 ☐ *true* ☐ *false*
18. Tick which would be best to measure the length of your table.

    ☐ *ruler* ☐ *trundle wheel* ☐ *metre stick*

19. y x $^3/_5$ = $^3/_5$ *so* y =
20. On the circle diagram, label the:

    radius **'x'**

    circumference **'y'**

    diameter **'z'**

    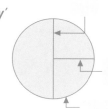

1. Simplify $^{10}/_{15}$.

2. $3.5 \div 0.5 =$

3. Complete the formulae: **diameter =** ___ **x** ___

4. 8 L 300 mL = $8^{300}/_{1\,000}$ L = 8. ___ L

5. $^{3}/_{5} + ^{4}/_{5} =$

6. $^{1}/_{2} \times ^{3}/_{4} =$

7. Write 2.08 million as a numeral.

8. 1 000, 3 000, 9 000, 27 000, ___

9. The chance of a baby being born a girl is
   ☐ 0% ☐ 50% ☐ 100%

10. What is the radius of a circle which has a 50 cm diameter? ___ cm

11. $a \div 3 = 5$ *so* $a =$ ___

12. $8^2 =$

13. Name this shape.

14. A shape has eight 2-cm by 2-cm faces. What is the shape's surface area? ___ cm^3

15. What is the place value of 7 in 3.067?

16. There are 6 euro to 10 Australian dollars. How many euro would you exchange for 20 Australian dollars?

17. Calculate the area of this sail. ___ m^2

6 m

4 m

18. Tick which would best measure the distance to the staff room.
   ☐ *ruler* ☐ *trundle wheel* ☐ *metre stick*

19. 9.38 km = ___ m

20. What is the average of 8, 10, 12?

1. $3.6 \div 0.6 =$

2. What is the volume of concrete needed to fill a hole 3 m by 2 m by 1 m? ___ m^3

3. Tick which scales would be best to weigh cooking ingredients.
   ☐ *kitchen scales* ☐ *bathroom scales*

4. Simplify $2^3/_9$.

5. Write 2.8 million as a numeral.

6. $^{1}/_{4} \times ^{1}/_{2} =$

7. A shape has eight 2-cm by 3-cm faces. What is the shape's surface area? ___ cm^3

8. What is the perimeter? ___ mm

12 mm
38 mm
40 mm
50 mm

9. There are 7 euro to 1 000 yen. How many euro would you exchange for 2 000 yen?

10. Reduce the line ⊢―――⊣ by 3:1. ___ mm

11. What is the place value of the 3 in 1.073?

12. $11^2 =$

13. Tick which would be best to measure the capacity of a bucket.
   ☐ *5 000 mL container*
   ☐ *1 000 mL jug*
   ☐ *100 mL beaker*

14. $y =$

80°
55°
y°

15. Circle the largest number.

   1 250 000   **1 500 000**

16. $^{1}/_{2} =$ ___ $/_{4} =$ ___ $/_{6} =$ ___ $/_{8}$

17. $a + 42\,000 = 60\,000$ *so* $a =$ ___

18. 7.72 t = ___ kg

19. 1.96, 1.97, 1.98, 1.99, ___

20. What is the average of 3, 4, 8, 8, 9?

WEDNESDAY

1. Write 6.057 million as a numeral.

2. $4.5 \div 0.9 =$

3. Simplify $3^{12}/_{15}$.

4. Complete the formulae: **diameter =**   x

5. What is the perimeter of this quadrilateral?

    mm

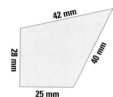

6. $^1/_2 \times ^1/_5 =$

7. Round 19.0509 to 3 decimal places =

8. What is the diameter of a circle with a radius of 1 m?

    m

9. Simplify 36 : 6 =   :

10.

    Reduce this line by 4:1.   mm

11. What is the meaning of 4 in 2.354?

12. Tick which would be best to measure the capacity of a teaspoon.
    ☐ 5 000 mL container
    ☐ 1 000 mL jug
    ☐ 100 mL beaker

13. $y - 15 = 25$ so $y =$

14. The angles in a quadrilateral add up to   .

15. 0.097, 0.098, 0.099,

16. What is the area of this sail?

    m^2

17. $^2/_3 + ^2/_3 + ^2/_3 =$

18. Write three capital letters that are symmetrical.

19. The area of the house is 400 m^2. What is the area of the garden?

    m^2

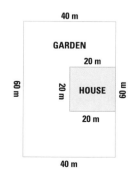

20. The perimeter of the house is 80 m. What is the perimeter of the garden?

    m

THURSDAY

1. $8.1 \div 0.9 =$

2. What is the area of this sail? m^2

3. Reduce this line ├────────┤ by 5:1.

    mm

4. Tick which scales would be best to weigh a full suitcase.
    ☐ kitchen scales   ☐ bathroom scales

5. Write 10.65 million as a numeral.

6. Simplify $^{20}/_{60}$.

7. $y \times 500 = 1\ 000$ so $y =$

8. 4 L 25 mL = $4^{25}/_{1\ 000}$ L = 4.   litres

9. $^2/_5 \times ^1/_2 =$

10.

    Show a 90° turn clockwise.

11. The chance of me reading a book this week is:
    ☐ 0%   ☐ 50%   ☐ 100%

12. What is the meaning of 5 in 3.245?

13. A shape has eight 1-cm by 5-cm faces. What is the shape's surface area? cm^3

14. $y° =$

15. 6 m =   mm

16. 3.85, 3.9, 3.95,

17. Draw a dot on co-ordinate (5,1) and label it 'A'.

18. Draw a dot on co-ordinate (1,5) and label it 'B'.

19. There are 0.6 euro to 1 Canadian dollar. How many euro would you exchange for 5 Canadian dollars?

20. Round 18.3678 to 3 decimal places.

MONDAY

1. Tick which would be best to measure the capacity of a watering can.
   - ☐ *5 000 mL container*
   - ☐ *1 000 mL jug*
   - ☐ *100 mL beaker*

2. Write $2^3/_4$ as an improper fraction.

3. Enlarge this line ⊢──┤ by 3:1. = _____ mm

4. 1 coin is tossed in the air.
   The outcome of how it lands is head and _____ .

5. $3.3 \div 0.3 =$

6. Complete the formulae: area = _____ x

7. $^1/_2 \times ^2/_5 =$

8. The chance that you will go to a different school next year is ☐ 0% ☐ 50% ☐ 100%.

9.
   y = _____

10. A shape has eight 2-cm by 4-cm faces. What is the shape's surface area? _____ cm³

11. How many faces on a hemisphere?

12. $80 + 80\,000 + 900 =$

13. Name this shape.

14. $^1/_2 > 0.358$ ☐ *true* ☐ *false*

15. $6\% = 0.$

16. 4 000, 400, 40, 4, _____

17. How many B boxes will fit into Box A?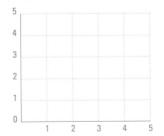

18. If there are ¥116 to €1.00, how many euro would you get for ¥348?

19. Draw a dot at co-ordinate (5,0) and label it 'A'.

20. Draw a dot at co-ordinate (2,4) and label it 'B'.

TUESDAY

1. $^1/_3 > 0.1$ ☐ *true* ☐ *false*

2. y = _____

3. $70 + 60\,000 + 200 =$

4. Change $8^3/_8$ to an improper fraction.

5. Round 6.789 to the nearest tenth.

6. One coin is tossed in the air. The outcome of how it lands is _____ and tail.

7. 8.03 m = _____ mm

8. 30% of €300.00 = € _____

9. Reduce this line ⊢────┤ by 2:1. _____ mm

10. If you are paid time and a half (normal rate is €8.00 per hour), what do you earn after 6 hours work?

    € _____

11. How many faces on an octahedron?

12. $9\% = 0.$

13.

    Draw to show a 180° turn clockwise.

14. 900, 90, 9, 0.9, _____

15. 7 L 7 mL = $7^7/_{1\,000}$ = 7. _____

The graph shows the number of rainy days for the first six months of a year.

16. Which month had 15 rainy days?

17. Which month had the most rainy days?

18. Which month had the least rainy days?

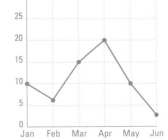

19. How many more rainy days had January than June?

20. Which month had 20 rainy days?

New wave mental maths   www.prim-ed.com   Prim-Ed Publishing

WEDNESDAY

1. $5\frac{1}{4} - \frac{3}{4} =$

2. $\frac{1}{5} < 0.1$ ☐ *true* ☐ *false*

3. $2.7 \div 0.3 =$

4. Complete the formulae: **diameter =**   **x**

5. Enlarge the line ├──┤ by 4:1.   mm

6. $\frac{1}{5} \times \frac{1}{2} =$

7. The chance of you sitting behind a boy in assembly is
   ☐ *0%* ☐ *50%* ☐ *100%*.

8. $y =$

9. Parts of South America are 4 hours behind GMT. If it is 3 a.m. in London, what time is it in South America?

10. Tick which container would be best to measure the capacity of a coffee mug.
    ☐ *3 000 mL container*
    ☐ *1 000 mL jug*
    ☐ *100 mL beaker*

11. $2.43 + 6.54 =$

12. Draw the rectangle to show a 540° turn anticlockwise.

13. $400 + 45\,000 + 7\,000 =$

14. $\frac{3}{10} =$ %

15. 4.04 kg =   g

16. $8.4, 8.6, 8.8,$

17. Two coins are tossed in the air. The outcomes of how they land are:

    head and

    head and

    tail and   .

18. 40% off a €100.00 item saves you €   .

19. Round 3.455 (nearest tenth).

20. If you are cycling at 30 km/hr, how far can you ride in 10 minutes?   km

THURSDAY

1. 125 000, 250 000, 375 000,

2. What is the perimeter?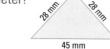
   mm

3. Tick which container would be best to measure the capacity of a large bottle.
   ☐ *5 000 mL container*
   ☐ *1 000 mL jug*
   ☐ *100 mL beaker*

4. $0.099 > \frac{1}{10}$ ☐ *true* ☐ *false*

5. Double 75.5.

6. $2.4 \div 0.6 =$

7. 9 L 99 mL = $\frac{999}{1\,000}$ L = 9.   litres

8. $\frac{1}{2} \times \frac{4}{5} =$

9. A shape has eight 3-cm by 4-cm faces. What is the shape's surface area?   cm³

10. Reduce this line ├──────┤
    by 6:1.   mm

11. If your normal rate is €10.00 per hour, how much do you earn after 6 hours at time and a half?

    €

12. There are 7 euro to 1 000 Japanese yen. How many euro would you exchange for 3 000 Japanese yen?

13. $3.5 - 0.8 =$

14. Double the shape.

15. $\frac{1}{5} + \frac{4}{5} + \frac{3}{5} =$

16. $\frac{7}{10} =$ %

17. 7.05 L =   mL

18. How many quarters in 3?

19. Round 6.372 (nearest tenth).

20. If you are cycling at 30 km/hr, how far will you ride in 20 minutes?   km

1. Tick which would be the best to measure the capacity of a barrel.
   - ☐ 5 000 mL container
   - ☐ 1 000 mL container
   - ☐ 100 mL container

2. $2.3 - 0.8 =$

3. $2.5 \div 0.5 =$

4. 35, 75, 115,

5. $80 + 700 + 2\,000 =$

6. $904\ kg = 0.$ ___ t

7. $^4/_5 \times ^1/_2 =$

8. The chance you will watch TV today.
   ☐ 0% ☐ 50% ☐ 100%

9. A shape has 10 2-cm by 2-cm faces. What is the shape's surface area? ___ cm³

10. Write in ascending order.

    0.05   0.3   2%

11. Round 0.375 (nearest tenth).

12. Write three capital letters that have more than one line of symmetry.

13. What is the area of this sail? ___ m²
    10 m
    5 m

14. There are 0.6 euro to 1 Canadian dollar. How many euro would you exchange for 3 Canadian dollars?

15. Simplify $^{15}/_{18}$.

16. Which would you use to measure the length of a pencil?
    ☐ mm ☐ cm ☐ m ☐ km

17. Draw the net of a triangular prism.

18. $10 \times$ ___ $= 8 \times 5$

19. The angles in a triangle add up to ___ °.

20. What is the ratio of boys to girls if there are 30 boys and 40 girls?

1. It is 10.30 a.m. in Ireland and 11.30 a.m. in France. What is the time difference?

2. $2^1/_2$, $2^3/_4$, $3^1/_4$, 4,

3. $4.1 + 0.9 =$

4. $3.6 \div 0.4 =$

5. $185\ cm =$ ___ m

6. Complete the formulae: **area =** ___ x

7. $^1/_2 \times ^6/_{10} =$

8. The chance a baby will be born a boy.
   ☐ 0% ☐ 50% ☐ 100%

9. What is the ratio of teachers to students if there are 30 teachers and 40 students?

10. $6\ L\ 35\ mL = 6^{35}/_{1\,000} = 6.$ ___ litres

11. Round 0.831 to the nearest tenth.

12. Which would you use to measure the weight of a child?
    ☐ g ☐ kg ☐ t

13. Draw the lines of symmetry on the equilateral triangle.

14. Write in descending order:

    0.11   0.3   20%

15. What is the area of this sail? ___ m²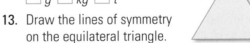
    12 m
    10 m

16. What is the perimeter of a pentagon with 6-cm sides? ___ cm

17. Write seven hundred and two thousand and forty-five as a numeral.

18. Write from smallest to largest.

    0.75   0.2   0.25   0.8

19. Simplify $^{20}/_{30}$.

20. If your standard pay is €9.00 per hour, what do you earn after doing 3 hours at time and a half?

    €

1. 300 x e = 2 700 *so* e =

2. 9, $9^1/_3$, 10, 11,

3. 2.1 ÷ 0.3 =

4. $^1/_4$ x $^8/_{10}$ =

5. The chance your teacher will grown an extra arm.
   ☐ *0%*   ☐ *50%*   ☐ *100%*

6. 8.3 + 0.7 =

7. Two coins are tossed in the air. The outcomes of how they land are:

   head and

   head and

   tail and

8. A shape has ten 1-cm by 3-cm faces. What is the shape's surface area?   cm^3

9. 40 + 70 000 + 9 =

10. There are 6 euro to 10 Australian dollars. How many euro would you exchange for 5 Australian dollars?

11. 8.96 − 5.05 =

12. What chance have you of going home early from school?
    ☐ *even*   ☐ *unlikely*   ☐ *very likely*
    ☐ *impossible*   ☐ *certain*

13.

    The area of the house is 1 200 m^2.
    What is the area of the garden?   m^2

14. The perimeter of the house is 140 m.
    What is the perimeter of the garden?   m

15. Which would you use to measure the weight of a ship? ☐ *g* ☐ *kg* ☐ *t*

16. What is the place value of the 5 in 48 250?

17. Will a parallelogram and an isosceles triangle tessellate together?

18. If you are cycling at 32 km/hr, how far do you travel in a quarter of an hour?   km

19. Simplify $^{15}/_{20}$.

20. 2, 4, 8, 16   Rule =

1. $3^1/_5$, $3^2/_5$, $3^4/_5$, $4^2/_5$,

2. Tick which would be best to measure the capacity of a bath.
   ☐ *5 000 mL container*
   ☐ *1 000 mL jug*
   ☐ *100 mL beaker*

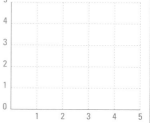

3. Draw a dot at co-ordinate (0,4) and label it 'A'.

4. Draw a dot at co-ordinate (2,5) and label it 'B'.

5. 4.9 ÷ 0.7 =

6. Complete the formulae: **diameter =   x**

7. 909 m = 0.   km

8. $^4/_5$ x $^1/_4$ =

9. 9 L 2 mL = $9^2/_{1 000}$ L = 9.

10. There are 7 euro to 1 000 Japanese yen. How many euro would you exchange for 4 000 yen?

11. Which would you use to measure the length of your classroom?
    ☐ *mm*   ☐ *cm*   ☐ *m*   ☐ *km*

12. 5.293 + 2.406 =

The pie chart shows the favourite colours of 6th Class pupils.

13. 32 pupils were surveyed. How many liked black?

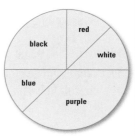

14. Is the number of pupils who liked red the same as the number who liked white?

15. What percentage of the class liked black?

16. What fraction of the class liked purple?

17. How many liked blue?

18. Simplify $3^{16}/_{20}$.

19. $^-2 + {}^-3 =$

20. If you are cycling at 18 km/hr, how far can you ride in 10 minutes?   km

1.

    Enlarge this line by 3:1. _____ mm

2. Which would you use to measure the amount of orange juice in a glass?

    ☐ mL   ☐ L

3. The chance of it getting dark tonight is:

    ☐ 0%   ☐ 50%   ☐ 100%

4. $6.5 \div 0.5 =$

5. $\frac{1}{2} \times \frac{4}{10} =$

6. A shape has ten 2-cm by 2-cm faces. What is the shape's surface area?   cm^3

7. Name this shape.

8. $\frac{8}{10} = 0.$

9. $29 \div 0.5 =$

10. $400 + 5 + 2\,000 + 60\,000 =$

11. There are 6 euro to 10 Australian dollars. How many euro would you exchange for 50 Australian dollars?

12. What would you use to measure the height of a house?

    ☐ mm   ☐ cm   ☐ m   ☐ km

13. 14.073 m = _____ mm

14. Complete the formulae: diameter = ___ x ___

15. Which numeral is the hundredth in 103.465?

16. Write $3\frac{1}{3}$ as an improper fraction.

17. What would you use to measure the weight of a chocolate bar?

    ☐ g   ☐ kg   ☐ t

18. What is the average of test scores 80, 35, 35?

19. A triangular prism has:

    _____ faces

    _____ edges

    _____ vertices

20. This is the net of a _____

    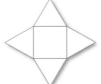

1. $\frac{2}{3} > \frac{1}{2}$ ☐ true   ☐ false

2. The chance of rolling an odd number on a dice is:

    ☐ 0%   ☐ 50%   ☐ 100%

3.

    Reduce this line by 2:1. _____ mm

4. $4.8 + 0.8 =$

5. 500, 50 000, 5 000 000, _____

6. Draw to show a rotation of 270° clockwise.

7. Draw a dot on co-ordinates (3,5), (5,2) and (1,2). Join them in order. What shape have you drawn?

    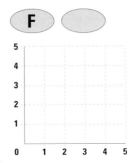

8. $\frac{1}{2} \times \frac{8}{10} =$

9. A shape has ten 1-cm by 3-cm faces. What is the shape's surface area?   cm^3

10. $6 + 1\,000 + 60\,000 =$

11. Write $\frac{19}{3}$ as a mixed number.

12. 19.356 kg = _____ g

13. What would you use to measure the weight of a cat?

    ☐ g   ☐ kg   ☐ t

14. Round 6.24 to 1 decimal place.

15. $\frac{2}{10} = 0.$

16. What is the perimeter of this pentagon? _____ mm

    9 mm

17. The circumference of a circle is approximately ☐ 2 ☐ 3 ☐ 4 times longer than the diameter.

18. If you are cycling at 28 km/hr, how far do you travel in 15 minutes? _____ km

19. Circle −6 on the number line.

    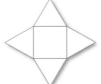

    Accu-matic Precision Instruments   Made in Ireland

    −8 −7 −6 −5 −4 −3 −2 −1 0 +1 +2 +3 +4 +5 +6 +7 +8

20. $(4 \times 5) - 8 =$

WEDNESDAY

1. 12 051 mL = _____ L

2. 3.6 ÷ 0.3 =

3. $4^1/_{10}$, $4^3/_{10}$, $4^7/_{10}$, $5^3/_{10}$, _____

4. 90 + 70 000 + 4 000 =

5. There are 7 euro to 1 000 Japanese yen. How many euro would you exchange for 5 000 Japanese yen?

6. $^4/_5 > 0.79$ ☐ true ☐ false

7. Complete the formulae: area = _____ x _____

8. How many edges on a pentagonal pyramid?

9. 60% = 0.6   ☐ true ☐ false

10. Draw the net of a cone.

11. Which would you use to measure the amount of water in a bucket?
    ☐ mL   ☐ L

12. y° =

13. $^4/_5 \times ^1/_2 =$

14. The time is 2.15 p.m. in Ireland and 3.15 p.m. in Spain. What is the time difference?

15. 1% = 0._____

16. Tick the largest   ☐ $^1/_2$ ☐ $^3/_4$ ☐ $^2/_6$

17. 1.3 + 0.7 =

18. $^1/_3 =$ _____ %

19. What is the floor area of a room 8 m by 6 m?
    _____ m²

20. Draw a dot on co-ordinates (1,3), (4,3), (4,1) and (1,1). Join them in order. What shape have you drawn?

THURSDAY

1. Which would you use to measure the amount of perfume in a bottle?
   ☐ mL   ☐ L

2. 4.8 ÷ 1.2 =

3. $^8/_{10} \times ^1/_4 =$

4. There are 0.6 euro to 1 Canadian dollar. How many euro would you exchange for 10 Canadian dollars?

5. What would you use to measure the length of an ant?
   ☐ mm   ☐ cm   ☐ m   ☐ km

6. The square root of 49 is _____.

7. How many degrees make up a triangle? _____°

8. Can an oval and a circle tessellate?

9. $5^3 = 5 \times 5 \times 5 =$

10. The factors of 8 are: 1, 2, 4 and 8. ☐ true ☐ false

11. 11, 15, 20, 26, _____

12. Area = _____ m²

12. Perimeter = _____ m

14. 3.25 = _____ %

15. 12 − 0.7 =

16. 4.1, 8.2, 16.4 = _____

17. Write the composite numbers between 11 and 20.
    _____ , _____ , _____ , _____ ,

    and _____

18. Which is heaviest?   (a) *0.4 t* (b) *80 kg* (c) *7 000 g*

19. Write 3.4 million as a numeral.

20. What is the average of the following?
    3, 5, 4, 7, 9, 4, 3

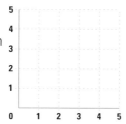

1. $3 \div 0.3 =$

2. $6 \times 8 =$

3. $60 \text{ mm} = 0.\underline{\hspace{2cm}} \text{m}$

4. Which would you use to measure the amount of pop in a can?
   ☐ *mL* ☐ *L*

5. What is the place value of three in 2.3 million?

6. $\frac{1}{2} \times \frac{2}{10} =$

7. How many vertices on a cube?

8. $4.05 + 0.85 =$

9. $(500 \div 25) \div 4 =$

10. $2.7 + 0.9 =$

11. There are 7 euro to 1 000 Japanese yen. How many euro would you exchange for 2 000 Japanese yen?

12. What would you use to measure the coast of Ireland?
    ☐ *mm* ☐ *cm* ☐ *m* ☐ *km*

13. 900, 2 700, 8 100,

14. What is the area of this sail?

    $\underline{\hspace{2cm}} \text{m}^2$

15. $750 \text{ mL} = \frac{3}{4} \text{ L} = 0.\underline{\hspace{2cm}}$ litres

16. Tick which you would use to measure the weight of a car.
    ☐ *g* ☐ *kg* ☐ *t*

17. Name this shape.

18. $50 \times a = 300$ *so* $a =$

19. 95% of €100.00 = €

20. What is the lowest common denominator of $\frac{3}{4}$ and $\frac{2}{10}$?

1. $(600 \div 25) \div 6 =$

2. How many vertices on a hemisphere?

3. $2.09 + 0.77 =$

4. $4.89 \text{ km} = \underline{\hspace{2cm}} \text{m}$

5. Is a square or a cube 2 dimensional?

6. $8.2 + 0.8 =$

7. $\frac{1}{3} \times \frac{3}{4} =$

8. What is the area of this sail?
   $\underline{\hspace{2cm}} \text{m}^2$

9. What is the place value of 9 in 3.09 million?

10. $1.8 \div 0.6 =$

11. Complete the formulae: **Area =**

12. 63 is a multiple of 9. ☐ *true* ☐ *false*

13. $2 \div \frac{1}{4} =$

14. $\underline{\hspace{2cm}}$, 0.99, 0.98, 0.97

The graph shows the average weight of children aged 8 – 12 at St. Mary's Primary school.

15. Which age has an average weight of 31 kg?

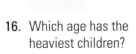

16. Which age has the heaviest children?

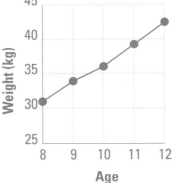

17. How much heavier are 11-year-olds than 10-year-olds?
    $\underline{\hspace{2cm}}$ kg

18. Which age has an average weight of 36 kg?

19. Based on this data would you expect the average weight of 7-year-olds to be < 30 kg or > 30 kg?
    $\underline{\hspace{2cm}}$ 30 kg

20. Would you expect the average weight of 13-year-olds to be <45 kg or > 45 kg?
    $\underline{\hspace{2cm}}$ 45 kg

WEDNESDAY

1. How many thousands in a million?
2. Which would you use to measure the amount of water in a watering can?

    ☐ mL ☐ L

3. $4.5 \div 0.9 =$
4. $6.04 + 0.79 =$
5. What is the place value of 2 in 2.45 million?

6. $102 - 42 =$

7. $\frac{6}{10} \times \frac{1}{2} =$
8. There are 0.6 euro to 1 Canadian dollar. How many euro would you exchange for 5 Canadian dollars?

9. How many vertices on a cone?

10. 1.15, 1.55, 1.95,

11. What would you use to measure the length of a pencil case?

    ☐ mm ☐ cm ☐ m ☐ km

12. 2.02 km = ___ m

13. Write the missing angle.

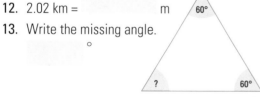

14. How many edges on a hemisphere?
15. Colour to $-3°$ on the thermometer.
16. Diameter of a circle = 3 cm. Therefore, the circumference

    is about ___ cm.

17. If a white board is 5 m long and 1.2 m high, what is its area?

    ___ m^2

18. What is the whiteboard's perimeter?

    ___ m

19. $(800 \div 25) \div 4 =$

20. 4 km $+ 300$ m = ___ m

THURSDAY

1. $\frac{1}{2} \times \frac{4}{5} =$

2. How many hundreds in a million?

3. Area = ___ m^2

4. Perimeter = ___ m
5. $\frac{1}{100} > \frac{1}{5}$ ☐ true ☐ false

6. $8, 8\frac{1}{3}, 9, 10, 11\frac{1}{3},$

7. 5 L 20 mL $= 5\frac{20}{1\,000}$ L $= 5.$ ___ litres
8. What is the place value of 8 in 3.78 million?

9. y =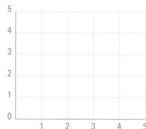

10. $(700 \div 25) \div 4 =$

11. Complete the formula: **diameter =**
12. Tick which you would use to measure the weight of a pencil.

    ☐ g ☐ kg ☐ t

13. The angles in a rectangle are all ___ .

14. How many vertices in a pentagonal prism?

15. Draw a dot on co-ordinates (3,5), (5,5), (5,3) and (3,3). Join them in order.

    What shape have you drawn?

16. Write $\frac{14}{3}$ as a mixed number.

17. The square root of 64 is ___ .

18. How many faces on a cube?

19. The LCD for $\frac{1}{8}$ and $\frac{1}{10}$ is ___ .

20. $6.4 \div 0.8 =$

1. 5.5 ÷ 1.1 =

2. 1.01 > 1.11

3. Enlarge this line ├───┤ by 3:1. _____ mm

4. Round 12.567 to 2 decimal places.

5. A cylinder has: _____ faces

    _____ edges

    _____ vertices

6. $\frac{1}{2} + \frac{1}{4} =$

7. 750 g = $\frac{3}{4}$ kg = 0._____ kg

8. 407 m = 0._____ km

9. $5^2 =$

10. 42 500 m = _____ km

11. Write $\frac{17}{7}$ as a mixed number.

12. 4% = 0._____

13. What would you use to measure the amount of medicine on a teaspoon?
    ☐ mL ☐ L

14. There are 7 euro to 1 000 Japanese yen. How many euro would you exchange for 3 000 Japanese yen?

15. Parts of the USA are 6 hours behind GMT. If it is 2.15 p.m. in London, what time is it in the USA?

16. If you are cycling at 36 km/hr, how far can you travel in $1\frac{1}{2}$ hours? _____ km

17. What would you use to measure the length of the playground?
    ☐ mm ☐ cm ☐ m ☐ km

18. If you normally earn €10.00 per hour and do 5 hours overtime at time and a half, how much should you earn?

    € _____

19. 650, 500, 350, _____

20. Round 25.4378 to 3 decimal places.

1. 2.009 < 2.07   ☐ true ☐ false

2. 1, 4, 9, 16, 25, _____

3. Kate scored $\frac{7}{10}$ in a spelling test. Write this as a percentage. _____ %

4. What would you use to measure the weight of a dog?
    ☐ g ☐ kg ☐ t

5. 29 000 mm = _____ m

6. Reduce the line ├──────┤ by 6.1.

    _____ mm

7. 0.4 x 0.3 =

8. $\frac{8}{10} - \frac{5}{10} =$

9. (3 x 4) + 2 =

10. y = _____ °

11. What type of triangle?

12. 245 m = $\frac{245}{1\,000}$ km = 0._____ km

13. ⁻6 + ⁻2 =

14. 0.3 x 0.9 =

15. 0.9 x 0.3 =

16. A car is travelling at 100 km/hr. How far can it travel in 30 minutes? _____ km

17. Write in ascending order.
    337   **996** $\frac{300}{1}$

18. Area = _____ cm²

19. Perimeter = _____ cm

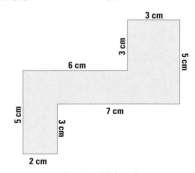

20. If you toss a coin, it will land

    on a _____ or _____ .

WEDNESDAY

1. $^4/_{10} + ^6/_{10} =$

2. $3.9 \div 1.3 =$

3. Circle the largest.

   50% of 30   **75% of 24**

4. 1.65 m =   cm

5. $75\% = ^3/_4 = 0.$

6. $6.007 > 6.069$ ☐ *true* ☐ *false*

7. $\div 5 = 30$

8. What is the name of the angle that is between 0° and 90°?

9. If you shake a dice it will land on a:

   ____ , ____ , ____ , ____ , ____ or ____ .

10. $7.95 - 2.04 =$

11. Reduce line ├──────┤ by 4:1.   mm

12. $4 + ^-8 =$

13. Jane scored 84% in a flute exam. Write this as a decimal.

14. A triangular prism =   faces

15. 9   18 = 27

16. Draw a net of a cube.

17. What would you use to measure the distance from Cork to Dublin?

    ☐ *mm* ☐ *cm* ☐ *m* ☐ *km*

18. $70\% = 0.07$ ☐ *true* ☐ *false*

19. $11^2 =$

20. $^1/_2 =$ %

THURSDAY

1. Halve $^1/_2$.

2. Write the missing angle.

3. What would you use to measure the amount of drink in a large pop bottle?

   ☐ *mL*   ☐ *L*

4. How many tenths in one?

5. ├────────┤
   x   y

   Enlarge line 'xy' by 2:1 =   mm

6. There are 0.6 euro to 1 Canadian dollar. How many euro would you exchange for 3 Canadian dollars?

7. What would you use to measure the weight of a banana?

   ☐ *g*   ☐ *kg*   ☐ *t*

8. $12^2 =$

9. $1.4 \times 0.4 =$

10. $10 - (18 \div 2) =$

11. Which 3-D shape has no edges or vertices?

12. 2m 15 cm = $2^{15}/_{100}$ m = 2.   m

13. Write $^{155}/_{1\,000}$ as a decimal.

14. $75\% = 0.$

15. $3.004 < 3.330$ ☐ *true* ☐ *false*

16. 3.3, 6.6, 9.9   Rule =

17. Write in descending order.

    $^8/_2$ **11** $1^1/_2$

18. Which is best value for money?

    ☐ *500 g coffee at €2.50*
    ☐ *1 kg coffee at €4.50*

19. $a + 1 = 1\,000\,000$ *so* a =

20. $2.8 \div 1.4 =$

MONDAY

1. $1.6 \div 0.2 =$

2. $(300 \div 25) \div 1 =$

3. $^4/_{10} \times ^1/_2 =$

4. Does an equilateral triangle have 2 or 3 equal sides and angles?

5. $5 \text{ km} + 400 \text{ m} =$ _____ km

6. A car costs €10 000 plus 20% VAT. What is the total price? €

7. Parts of Africa are 2 hours behind GMT. If it is 8.30 a.m. in London, what time is it in Africa?

8. $(8 \quad 3) \quad 6 = 30$

9. What would you use to measure the length of a chocolate bar?
   ☐ mm ☐ cm ☐ m ☐ km

10. $7 + ^-4 =$

11. Is a heptagon or a hexagon a 7-sided shape?

12. $0.8 \times 0.3 =$

13. $5 \text{ m } 40 \text{ cm} = 5^{40}/_{100} \text{ m} = 5.$ _____ m

14. Simplify the ratio. $3:15 = 1:$

15. How many tenths in 2?

16. $6^2 =$

17. Draw the axes of symmetry on the hexagon.

18. 3, 10, 17, 24,

19. Is 24 a multiple of 2 and 3?

20. $2.02 > 2.2$ ☐ true ☐ false

TUESDAY

1. A shape has six 2-cm by 4-cm faces. What is the shape's surface area? cm³

2. Write 6.5 million as a numeral.

3. $8.2 + 0.8 =$

4. What would you use to measure the weight of a sheep?
   ☐ g ☐ kg ☐ t

5. What is the chance of rain today?

6. There are 6 euro to 10 Australian dollars. How many euro would you exchange for 5 Australian dollars?

7. If you rode your bike at 30 km/hr for an hour and a half, how far would you have travelled?
   _____ km

8. What will I pay for a €60 coat if there is a 33% reduction? €

9. 2, 20, 200, _____, 20 000

10. $80 + 700 + 8 000 =$

11. $^-4 + ^+7 =$

12. Round 18.0765 to 3 decimal places.

13. $1 \text{ m} + 45 \text{ cm} =$ _____ m

14. Rotate 270° clockwise.

15. Claire is travelling at 60 km/hr. How long will it take to travel 1 km?
    _____ minutes

16. $(400 \div 25) \div 4 =$

17. The place value of 8 in 48 250 is _____.

18. $5a + 10 = 20$ $a =$

19. $8.5 + 1.5 =$

20. $600 \text{ mL} = ^6/_{10} \text{ L} = 0.$ _____ litres

1. What would you use to measure the amount of water in a sink?
   ☐ mL ☐ L

2. There are 7 euro to 1 000 Japanese yen. How many euro would you exchange for 4 000 Japanese yen?

3. The angles in a triangle are 75° and 80°. What is the 3rd angle?   °

4. What is the chance of the temperature exceeding 15° C today?

5. The total cost of 3 pens is 48c. What is the average cost of a pen?   c

6. Draw the net of a tetrahedron.

7. What do we call an angle that is between 180° and 360°?

8. 50, 500,   , 50 000

9. 8.7 + 1.3 =

10. Tick the largest:
    ☐ 20% of 100   ☐ 50% of 50

11. Write 8.9 million as a numeral.

12. 1.7 x 0.3 =

13. 8 km + 700 m =   km

14. If you ride your bike for 15 minutes and travelled 7 km, what speed were you travelling?   km/hr

15. 0.01 < 0.1   ☐ true ☐ false

16. 2 000 + 90 + 500 =

17. $4^2/_{10}$ =   (decimal)

18. Tick which scales would be best to weight a banana.
    ☐ kitchen scales   ☐ bathroom scales

19. Simplify $^{15}/_{18}$.

20. 5 x y = 300 so y =

1. What is the chance of you doing maths on the last day of school?

2. $^+7 - {}^-5$ =

3. Double 5.5 =

4. 7.2 ÷ 0.9 =

5. $^1/_2$ x $^2/_{10}$ =

6. 4 kg 55 g = $4^{55}/_{1\,000}$ kg = 4.   kg

7. 2^5 =

8. 7.3 + 1.7 =

9. The time is 9.30 a.m. in Ireland and 2.30 p.m. in India. What is the time difference?

10. What would you use to measure the amount of water in an ice-cube tray?
    ☐ mL   ☐ L

11. Draw a dot on co-ordinates (2,4), (3,4), (4,3), (4,2), (3,1), (2,1), (1,2) and (1,3). Join them in order.

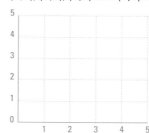

What shape have you drawn?

12. Which digit in the decimal 5.067 is the hundredth?

13. Are 450 and 402 both prime numbers?   °

14. How many degrees in a triangle?

15. 8, 16, 32, 64,

16. 0.5 < 1   ☐ true ☐ false

17. 20 + 900 + 3 000 =

18. Simplify $^{15}/_{20}$.

19. 87.5% = $^7/_8$ = 0.

20. Tick which would be best to measure the length of a pen.
    ☐ ruler   ☐ trundle wheel   ☐ metre stick

1. Round 5.79 to one decimal place.

2. Write one million and ten as a numeral.

3. Write the prime number that comes after 11.

4. The circumference of a circle is approximately ☐ *2* ☐ *3* ☐ *4* times longer than the diameter.

5. Simplify $^{15}/_{20}$.

6. If a clock shows 9 o'clock, what is the angle? ☐ *45°* ☐ *90°* ☐ *9°*

7. $20 = (5 + a)$ *so* $a =$

8. $5 \overline{)205} =$

9. $8 \times {}^2/_4 =$

10. Circle –5 on the number line.

11. $4^2 =$

12. This is the net of a

13. 30% of €100 =

    €

14. $^3/_4 + {}^3/_4 =$

15. $(5 \times 4) + 5 =$

16. Round $7^3/_7$.

17. Name this shape.

18. $(4 + 8) \times (3 + 3) =$

19. A cube has:

    faces

    edges

    vertices

20. Tick the largest ☐ $^3/_4$ ☐ $^5/_{10}$ ☐ $^2/_8$

21. The time is 9.20 a.m. in Ireland and 10.20 a.m. in Germany. What is the time difference?

22. $^1/_5 =$ %

23. $4^3 = 4 \times 4 \times 4 =$

24. What is the 24-hour time for 8.00 p.m.?

    hours

25. Write the numeral twenty three point one.

1. Write the numeral twenty five point two.

2. Round 8.57 to one decimal place.

3. The area of an oblong field 100 m by 40 m =

    m²

4. Name this shape.

5. Circle –3 on the number line.

6. This is the net of a

7. What would be the diameter of a circle if its radius is 5 cm?

    cm

8. $(8 \times 4) - 2 =$

9. The time is 7 a.m. in Ireland and 9 a.m. in South Africa. What is the time difference?

10. $80 + b = 50 \times 3$

    so $b =$

11. 250, 500, , 1 000

12. Write the composite number that comes after 17.

13. 40% of €60.00 =

    €

14.
    Draw a 270° turn anticlockwise.

15. Round 7.6.
    (Nearest whole number)

16. Perimeter of a regular pentagon with 7 cm sides =

    cm

17. What is the LCD for $^3/_4$ and $^1/_2$?

18. The meaning of 4 in 411 200?

19. Simplify $^{12}/_{15}$.

20. Name this shape.

21. Name this shape.

22. $7 - 0.3 =$

23. If there are £0.60 (UK) to €1.00, how many euro would you get for £6.00 (UK)?

24. If a lolly jar contains 20 lollies in total, 4 red, 10 yellow and 6 orange, what chance have you of picking a red lolly?

    in

25. What is the place value of 6 in 617 000?

1. $10^2 =$
2. If there are £0.60 (UK) to €1.00, how many euro would you get for £12.00 (UK)?

3. $^3/_5 + {}^4/_5 =$
4. $5 - 0.02 =$
5.
   How many B boxes would fit into Box A?

6. The factors of 10 are

   _____ , _____ ,

   and _____

7. $2^5 = 2 \times 2 \times 2 \times 2 \times 2 =$

8. Round 7.07 to the nearest tenth

9. Tick the smallest
   ☐ $^1/_3$ ☐ $^8/_9$ ☐ $^3/_6$

10. An architect has drawn your new house plans. Your dining room window measures 12 m long and is drawn as 12 cm in length on paper. What is the scale?
    ☐ 1:12   ☐ 1:1
    ☐ 1:100

11. Circle –3 on the number line.

    Accu-matic Precision Instruments
    –6 –5 –4 –3 –2 –1 0 +1 +2 +3 +4 +5 +6

12. $(7 \times 6) - (2 \times 11) =$

13. What is the volume of a room 2 m wide, 4 m long and 3 m high?

    _____ m³

14. A store has a 10% discount. What should you pay for an item tagged at €80.00?

    € _____

15. What is the size of this angle?

    _____ °

16. The time is 8 p.m. in Ireland and 9 p.m. in Libya. What is the time difference?

17. $^3/_5 =$ _____ %

18. $25 \times {}^4/_5 =$

19. Write one million, one thousand and eleven as a numeral.

20. $29.5 \div 10 =$

21. Draw a line to show the diameter on this circle.

22. What is the place value of the 2 in 2 411 333?

23. If a clock shows 6 o'clock, what is the size of the angle?

    _____ °

24. What is the LCD for $^2/_3$ and $^1/_5$?

25. A cylinder has:

    faces _____

    edges _____

    vertices _____

1. Write the prime numbers between 21 and 30.

   _____ and _____

2. $8 \overline{)408} =$
3. 50% off a €700 item, new price =

   € _____

4. Name this 3-D shape.

5. Write the numeral three hundred and twelve point two.

6. The diameter of a circle is 20 cm. What is the radius?

   _____ cm

7. $2.60 > 2.06$
   ☐ *true* ☐ *false*

8. $a + 55 = 100$ *so* $a =$

9. $36 \times {}^3/_9 =$

10. Round 9.98 to the nearest tenth.

11. $(7 \times 5) - (10 \div 2) = 40$
    ☐ *true* ☐ *false*

12. Is 253 divisible by 9?

13. The factors of 14 are

    _____ , _____ ,

    and _____

14.
    How many B boxes will fit into Box A evenly?

15. Double $^1/_4$.

16. $10^5 =$

17. $6 {}^1/_5 - {}^3/_5 =$

18. If there are £0.60 (UK) to €1.00, how many euro would you get for £30.00 (UK)?

19. $^6/_8 =$ _____ %

20. What is the probability of being born on a Wednesday?

    _____ in _____

21. A pentagonal prism has:

    faces _____

    edges _____

    vertices _____

22. Simplify $^{21}/_{24}$.

23. What is the ratio of boys to girls if there are 9 boys and 18 girls?

24. How many halves in 4?

25. 19 is a multiple of 3.
    ☐ *true* ☐ *false*

1. The factors of 21 are
    , ,
    and

2. 25% of 900 =

3. Write one million, one thousand and one as a numeral.

4. 73.55 ÷ 10 =

5. 6 x b = 42

   so b =

6. ▶

   Show as a 90° turn anticlockwise.

7. What is the volume of a box 40 cm by 20 cm by 30 cm?

   cm³

8. 35 x $^3/_5$ =

9. What is the LCD of $^3/_{10}$ and $^3/_4$?

10. On your house plans a measurement of 15 m is indicated for a fence. If the scale is 1:100, how long should the line be on your plans?

    cm

11. Halve $^1/_2$.

12. Octahedron = faces

13. The place value of 2 in 0.32.

14. How many halves in 6?

15. Add brackets to this number sentence.
    8 x 3 − 45 ÷ 9 = 19

16. 16, 32, 64,

17.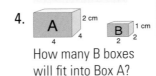
    How many B boxes will fit into Box A?

18. $5^3/_{10} - ^7/_{10}$ =

19. Name this shape.

20. 49 is a multiple of 7.
    ☐ *true* ☐ *false*

21. If the diameter of a circle is 28 cm, what is the radius?

    cm

22. 9.1, 9.05, 9,
    , 8.9, 8.85

23. A bus timetable shows 8-minute intervals between each stop. If a bus leaves the depot at 6.04 a.m. and has 3 stops, what time will it be at its final destination?

    a.m.

24. 10⁵ =

25. Circle −3 on the number line.

    Accu-mate Precision instruments
    −6 −5 −4 −3 −2 −1 0 +1 +2 +3 +4 +5 +6

1. The square root of 16 is

2. Write these decimals from smallest to largest.
   0.5   0.75   0.05
   , ,

3. What is the ratio of boys to girls if there are 12 boys and 24 girls?

4.
   How many B boxes will fit into Box A?

5. $^1/_4$ kg = g

6. c x 12 = 132

   so c =

7. What is the area of a floor 7 m by 6 m?

   m²

8. 9 − 0.01 =

9. How many faces on a hemisphere?

10. How many thirds in 4?

11. 7)‾427‾ =

12. Write twelve forty in the morning in 24-hour time.

    hours

13. 7.07 > 7.70
    ☐ *true* ☐ *false*

14. Write these fractions from largest to smallest.
    $^1/_2$ $^8/_{10}$ $^2/_5$

    , ,

15. Double 0.8.

16. The angles in a rectangle are all how many degrees?
    °

17. Round 32.83 to the nearest tenth.

18. 38.5 ÷ 10 =

19. Your house plans are drawn using 1:100 as the scale. Measure this line and indicate the actual length in metres.

    ├─────────────┤

    m

20. $^2/_5$ = %

21. Name this shape.

22. $7^6/_8 + 2^4/_8$ =

23. This is the net of a

24. 75% of 500 =

25. A jar contains 3 chocolate chip, 12 coconut and 5 ginger biscuits. Without looking, what is the probability of choosing a ginger biscuit?

    in

1. The square root of 100 is

2. Write these decimals from smallest to largest.

   0.5　　**0.05**　　**0.005**

   _____ , _____ ,

3. 3 − 0.94 =

4. 2.85, 2.9, 2.95, _____

5. 15% of €60.00 =

   €

6. How many quarters in 3?

7. Write the missing angle.

8. Write one million, one hundred and ten as a numeral.

9. What is the volume of a room 7 m by 3 m by 2 m?

   m³

10.

    Which angle is a right angle?

11. Round 23.58 to the nearest tenth.

12.

    How many B boxes will fit into Box A?

13. 3.004 = 3.04

    ☐ *true*　☐ *false*

14. 50 000 − c = 35 000

    so c =

15.

    Draw as a 180° turn clockwise.

16. Write eleven fifty two at night in 24-hour time.

    _____ hours

17. The average of these numbers, **8, 9, 4, 7, 12**

    is

18. A floor needs recarpeting. The room is 8 m by 5 m. How many square metres is needed?

    m²

19. The next prime number after 23 is

20. Add brackets to this number sentence.

    7 x 8 ÷ 4 x 2 = 7

21. ³/₅ kg = _____ g

22. This is the net of a

23. What is the radius of a circle with a 15-cm diameter?

    cm

24. Write seven hundredths as a decimal.

25. Diameter of a circle = 4 cm. Therefore, the circumference is about

    cm

1. Write 2²/₃ as an improper fraction.

2. 10 − 0.92 =

3. What is the perimeter of a block of land 50 m by 25 m?

   m

4. Name this shape.

5. c ÷ 3 = 300

   so c =

6. What is the area of a piece of paper 50 cm by 20 cm?

   cm²

7. 0, 1, 1, 2, 3, 5, _____ , 13, 21

8. The square root of 100 is

9. 2.97, 2.98, 2.99, _____

10. 15% of 40 =

11. Write ¹/₁₀ as a decimal.

12. (70 x 10) ÷ (5 x 2) =

13. The next composite number after 21 is

    .

14. Write the missing angle.

15. How many quarters in 3?

16. 6.03 + 6.003 =

17. The average of these numbers, **52, 45, 50, 55, 48** is

    .

18. 5²/₅ − ⁴/₅ =

19. ⁴/₅ kg = _____ g

20. This is the net of a

21. Write the numeral eighteen point zero four.

22. What is the chance of picking a king from a deck of playing cards?

    in

23. What is the perimeter of a fence on a rectangular block 25 m in width and 35 m in length?

    m

24. 5 ⁷/₁₀ + 3 ⁹/₁₀ =

25. How many B boxes will fit into Box A?

    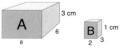

1. Write $^9/_4$ as a mixed number.

2. The square root of 64 is

3. Place value of 5 in 2.965?

4. Write $^7/_{10}$ as a decimal.

5. Write the missing angle.

120° 120°
60° ?
°

6. The diameter of a circle is 9 cm. What is the radius?

_____ cm

7. 90, 140, 640, _____ , 55 640

8. The factors of 28 are:

_____ , _____ ,

_____ , _____ ,

and _____

9. This is the net of a

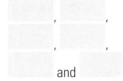

10. Simplify $^{15}/_{24}$.

11. Circle the prime number.

30   31   32

12. y x 700 = 70 000

so y =

13. Write $^{75}/_{100}$ as a decimal.

14. $7^5/_7 + 4^6/_7 =$

15. Write $2^2/_3$ as an improper fraction.

16.

Draw as a 270° turn anticlockwise.

17. Write the numeral twelve point zero four.

18. Write these decimals from smallest to largest.

1.4   0.04   0.44

_____ , _____ ,

_____

19. Name this 3-D shape.

20. How many quarters in 3?

21. The average of these numbers, 4, 6, 3, 0, 2 is

22. Name this shape.

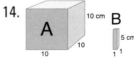

23. What is the volume of a sea container 15 m x 4 m x 2 m?

_____ m³

24. What is the ratio of girls to boys if there are 20 girls and 5 boys?

25. $^3/_4$ kg = _____ g

1. Write $2^2/_3$ as an improper fraction.

2. What is the meaning of 7 in 7 350 000?

3. $2 \div ^1/_3 =$

4. The square root of 81 is

5. Write $^4/_{10}$ as a decimal.

6. 25% of 10 =

7. 3.7 – 0.9 =

8. Write the numeral fourteen point zero four.

9. 0.9 + 0.6 =

10. Write $^{10}/_3$ as a mixed number.

11. y x 50 = 3 000

so y =

12. The diameter of a circle is 15 cm. What is the radius?

_____ cm

13. 2.6, 3.2, 3.8, _____

14.

A   10 cm   B
10   5 cm
10   1   1

How many B boxes will fit evenly into Box A?

15. What is the perimeter of a regular hexagon with 6 cm sides?

_____ cm

16. Double 3.7.

17. What is the LCD for $^2/_5$ and $^3/_4$?

18. Write the missing angle.

90°
110°   110°
°
?

19. The factors of 18 are:

_____ , _____ ,

_____ , _____ ,

and _____

20. How many degrees?

°

21. This is the net of a

22. Write these decimals from smallest to largest.

0.9   0.09   1.9

_____ , _____ ,

_____

23. How many quarters in 3?

24. $^1/_5$ kg = _____ g

25. The time is 4.15 p.m. in Ireland and 11.15 a.m. in New York. What is the time difference?

1. Circle the largest number.

   45 005   **45 050**

2. $40 + y = 130$

   so y =

3. $2^2 + 6^2 =$

4. $^3/_5 + ^3/_5 =$

5. Round 1.47 to the nearest tenth.

6. If there are $0.90 (US) to €1.00, how many euro would you get for $1.80 (US)?

7. 3, 8, 15, 24,

8. 10% of €30.00 =

   €

9. Write $1^1/_5$ as an improper fraction.

10. The square root of 100 is

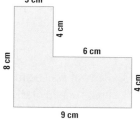

11. Area =   cm²

12. Perimeter =

                cm

13. A tossed coin has a

        in   chance of landing on a 'tail'.

14. Write three hundred and thirty thousand as a numeral.

15. What is the average of these test scores: **8, 5, 9, 2**?

16. What is the angle of north to east?
    °

17. The temperature is −2 °C. What will it be if it rises by 5 °C?

    °C

18. What is the chance of a bee flying into your classroom today?
    (a) *impossible*
    (b) *unlikely*
    (c) *even*
    (d) *very likely*
    (e) *certain*

19. What is the ratio of pink sweets to yellow sweets if there are 5 pink sweets and 15 yellow sweets?

20. $2 ÷ ^1/_5 =$

21. $10 \times \quad = 20 \times 2$

22. Draw the net of a cuboid.

23. $^4/_{20} =$ %

24. $30 ÷ 0.5 =$

25. $75\% > ^3/_4$
    ☐ *true* ☐ *false*

1. 400 g = $^2/_5$ kg =

   0.   kg

2. What is the average of **10, 12, 8, 10**?

3. A strip of land is 2 ha in size and is 1 000 m

   by   m.

4. Draw the net of a tetrahedron.

5. Parts of Australia are 8 hours ahead of GMT. If it is 8.15 a.m. in London, what time is it in Australia?

6. $10^2 − 5^2 =$

7. Write $3^2/_3$ as an improper fraction.

8. 0.3 =   %

9. 9, 18, 27, 36

   Rule =

10. 20% of €70.00 =

    €

11. $90 + 70 = 2 \times y$

    so y =

12. $6 ÷ ^1/_2 =$

13. Write $^{14}/_5$ as a mixed number.

14.

    Imagine the triangle has been turned 270° clockwise. Circle its new position.

15. The angles in a triangle add up to
    °

16. $10^5 =$

17. Circle the smallest number.

    507 025   **57 025**

18. The square root of 49 is

19. Write $^{25}/_{100}$ as a decimal.

20. Round 6.73 to one decimal place.

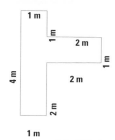

21. Area =   m²

22. Perimeter =

                m

23. Draw a shape double the dimensions of this oblong shape and show the new measurements.

24. Draw the axes of symmetry on this pentagon.

25. The temperature is −4 °C. What will it be if it rises by 3 °C?

1. 750 g = $^3/_4$ kg = _____ kg

2. $2^3/_5$ = _____ (improper fraction)

3. List the possible outcomes of tossing a coin.
_____ and _____

4. Simplify $^{14}/_{20}$.

5. Circle the smallest number.
505 025   505 250

6. 0.3, 0.6, 0.9, 1.2
Rule = _____

7. The square root of 100 is _____

8. 8% = $^8/_{100}$ = 0._____

9. Round 4.026 to 2 decimal places. _____

10. Write the numeral five hundred and five thousand and fifty-five. _____

11. Diameter of a circle with a radius of 3 cm = _____ cm

12. If there are $0.90 (US) to €1.00, how many euro would you get for $2.70 (US)? _____

13. If a car travels 5 km in 10 minutes, how far can it go in 1 hour? _____ km

14. Parts of the USA are 6 hours behind GMT. If it is 3.35 p.m. in London, what time is it in the USA?

15. The temperature is –4 °C. What will it be if it rises by 7 °C?

16. Draw the axes of symmetry on this octagon.

17. $^3/_4$ + y = 1
so y = _____

18. Write $^{17}/_3$ as a mixed number. _____

19. 2.02 < 2.1
☐ *true*   ☐ *false*

20. Round 4.072 to the nearest hundredth. _____

21. A house plan scale is 1:100 and a room measures 2 000 mm by 4 000 mm. How many square metres is the room? _____ m²

22. Write $^5/_{100}$ as a decimal. _____

23. How many quarters in 5? _____

24. Draw the net of a tetrahedron.

25. 5 ÷ $^1/_2$ = _____

1. 4.25 + 2.5 = _____

2. If there are ¥116 to €1.00, how many euro would you get for ¥580?

3. $^3/_5$ kg = 0.6 kg = _____ g

4. Circle the largest.
5% of 40   20% of 50

5. Draw a shape double the dimensions of this oblong. Show new measurements.
2 _____ 5

6. How many times has the area increased? _____

7. The average of **6**, **11**, **12** and **15** is _____

8. 250, 1 000, 4 000, 16 000, _____

9. 15% of €30.00 = € _____

10. 345 m = $^{345}/_{1\,000}$ m = 0._____ km

11. 2^5 = _____

12. 8.2, 8, 7.8, 7.6
Rule = _____

13. List the possible outcomes of tossing a coin.
_____ and _____

14. y = _____

15. A room measures 4 000 mm by 5 500 mm and the plan has a scale of 1:100. On paper, using the scale, it measures 40 mm by _____ mm.

16. Round 10.298 to 2 decimal places. _____

17. Draw the axes of symmetry on the isosceles triangle.

18. Double $^1/_4$.

19. Radius = _____ cm

20. Draw the net of a cylinder.

21. Halve $^1/_2$.

22. Write $^{22}/_4$ as a mixed number. _____

23. Parts of Africa are 2 hours ahead of GMT. If it is 11.15 p.m. in London, what time is it in Africa? _____

24. If a car travels 11 km in 10 minutes, how far can it go in 1 hour? _____ km

25. y × 7 = 14
so y = _____

1. 2.25 + 3.4 =
2. Diameter of a circle with a radius of 10 cm

   =   cm
3. Mark scored $^8/_{10}$ in a maths test. Write this as a percentage.

             %
4. $620 = {}^{620}/_{1\,000}$ km =

   0.   km
5. 24   2 = 12
6. Draw a net of a cone.

7. $3^6/_{10} + 2^7/_{10}$ =

8. 25% of €40.00 =

   €
9. 10, 20, 30, 40

   Rule =
10. The time is 10.15 a.m. in Ireland and 11.15 a.m. in France. What is the time difference?

11. Which is the best value for money?
    ☐ 250 g sugar at €1.40
    ☐ 750 g sugar at €4.00
12.

    Show a double of this shape and write the new measurements.

13. Circle the largest.
    10% of 90   20% of 50
14. Write $^3/_9$ as an improper fraction.

15. y° =

    145°
16. A farm block is 500 m by 800 m. What is the area?

                 m²
17. The square root of 81 is

18. 15% = 0.
19.

    ∃
    E
    ▷

    Turn the rectangle 180° clockwise. Draw the new shape.
20. Round 16.659 to 2 decimal places.

21. Draw the axes of symmetry on the hexagon.
22. If there are ¥116 to €1.00, how many euro would you get for ¥1 160?

23. Halve 5.8.
24. If a car is travelling at 100 km/hr, how far does it travel in 15 minutes?

                 km
25. $6 \div {}^1/_3$ =

1. If there are $0.90 (US) to €1.00, how many euro would you get for $7.20 (US)?

2. 9.58 – 2.05 =
3. $7^3/_4 + 2^3/_4$ =

4. If you double the dimensions of this rectangle, how many times does the area increase by?
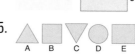
   4
   3
5.

   A B C D E

   Which shapes have 3 lines of symmetry?

        and
6. The LCD for $^1/_2$ and $^1/_3$

   is   .
7. Eilish scored $^7/_{10}$ in a spelling test. Write this as a percentage.

        %
8. 249 m = $^{249}/_{1\,000}$ km =

   0.   km
9. Place value of 3 in 371 929 =

10. 6   6 = 36
11. 5.1, 10.2, 15.3

    Rule =
12. 70% of €90.00?

    €
13. $y + 7^1/_2 = 8$

    so y =

14. Which is the best value for money?
    ☐ 800 g sugar at €1.20
    ☐ 1 kg sugar at €1.40
15. Parts of South America are 4 hours behind GMT. If it is 3.15 a.m. in London, what time is it in South America?

16. Circle the largest.
    20% of 40   25% of 35
17. Write $^{19}/_4$ as a mixed number.

18. 2^6 =
19.

    Draw a 270° turn clockwise.

20. $5 \div {}^1/_2$ =
21.

    a°
    50°
    o

    a =
22. 85% = 0.8
    ☐ *true* ☐ *false*
23. Draw the net of a tetrahedron.

24. Round 0.153 to the nearest hundredth.

25. If there are 2 000 West Toast Pigeons fans and 200 Sydney Ducks fans, what is the ratio of Pigeon to Duck fans?

1. 9.86 − 4.23 =

2. $y + {}^{33}/_7 = 5$

   so y =

3. 3.04 =   %

4. If the diameter of a circle is 10 cm, what is the radius?

   cm

5. 25% of €200.00 =

   €

6. $6 + {}^-3 =$

7. Which of the following numbers is a prime number?

   6   7   8

8. 600, 60, 6,

9. What is the meaning of 5 in 5 172 996?

10. Kelly scored 62% in a spelling test. Write this as a decimal.

11. The average of these numbers, **25, 20, 30, 35, 15**

   is

12. Draw the net of a cylinder.

13. 630 m = ${}^{630}/_{1\,000}$ km =

   0.   km

14. 0.3 x 0.8 =

15.

   Draw a 90° turn clockwise.

16. 20   25 = 45

17.

   Turn the rectangle 90° anticlockwise. Draw the new position.

18. 70, 63, 56, 49

   Rule =

19. $9 \div {}^1/_2 =$

20. Circle the largest.

   750 220   7 150 220

21. 1% = 0.01

   ☐ *true* ☐ *false*

22. 2 x   = 24 ÷ 3

23. If a car takes 20 minutes to travel 15 km, how fast is it going?

   km/hr

24. Which is the best value for money?

   ☐ *€600 carpet with 25% off*

   ☐ *€750 carpet with 33% off*

25. How many B boxes will fit into Box A?

1. What is the probability of selecting an odd number card from a deck?

   in

2. Round 0.639 to the nearest tenth.

3. ${}^2/_3 > {}^1/_5$

   ☐ *true* ☐ *false*

4. 0.6 x 0.3 =

5. What is the volume of a room 10 m x 7 m x 3 m?

   m³

6. Sam scored 70% in a maths test. Write this as a decimal.

7. Halve ${}^1/_2$.

8. 6 m 25 cm = $6{}^{25}/_{100}$ m

   = 6.   m

9. 6.2 + y = 7.9

   so y =

10. 3   8 = 24

11. 1, 4, 16, 64,

             , 1 024

12. $7{}^9/_{10} + {}^3/_{10} =$

13. 8% = 0.08

   ☐ *true* ☐ *false*

14. Draw the axes of symmetry on the octagon.

15. Write ${}^{650}/_{1\,000}$ as a decimal.

16. Circle the largest.

   500 250   5 025 250

17. 8.27 − 2.05 =

18. 20.8, 15.6, 10.4

   Rule =

19. a =

   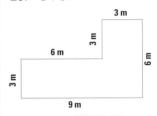

20. ${}^-9 + 3 =$

21. Area =   m²

22. Perimeter =

   m

23. If you measure a wall at 9 m and draw it using a scale of 1:100, how many mm long is it on the plan?

   mm

24. Which is the best value for money?

   ☐ *€800 settee with 20% off*

   ☐ *€900 settee with 33% off*

25. Draw the net of a triangular prism.

1. 0.9 x 0.4 =

2. 4 + ⁻7 =

3. 7.07 ≠ 7.70

   ☐ *true* ☐ *false*

4. 42% = 0.　　　 =

   /$_{100}$

5. 9 m 45 cm = $9^{45}/_{100}$ cm

   = 9.

6. A car is travelling at 100 km/hr. If it makes no stops and travels for 650 km, how long does the trip take?

   　　　 hours

7. Write one million, one thousand and ten as a numeral.

8. (18 ÷ 2) ÷ (3 x 1) =

9. 36　　　 4 = 9

10. Name this shape.

11. How many axes of symmetry does it have?

12. Write $^8/_{1\,000}$ as a decimal.

13. Circle the largest.

    4 750 500   4 500 700

14. 10.34 + 25 + 24 =

15.

    aº   75º

    o

    a =

16. 100 000 = y⁵ *so* y =

17. Which is the best value for money?

    ☐ *250 g flour at €1.20*

    ☐ *750 g flour at €3.10*

18. Is 81 a multiple of 8?

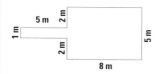

5 m 2 m

1 m

2 m   5 m

8 m

19. Area =　　　 m²

20. Perimeter =

    　　　 m

21.

    Draw a 180º turn clockwise.

22. 50.8, 40.6, 30.4

    Rule =

23. 250 g = $^1/_4$ kg =

    0.　　　 kg

24. How many faces on an octahedron?

25. If you draw a wall using a scale of 1:100 and it measures 20 mm, what is the actual length?

    　　　 m

1. 3 + ⁻7 =

2. 0.6 x 0.3 =

3. 8 m 35 cm = $^{835}/_{100}$ cm

   = 8.　　　 cm

4. Name this triangle.

5. $^3/_4$ ≠ 0.75

   ☐ *true* ☐ *false*

6. What is the area of a floor 12 m by 4 m?

   　　　 m²

7. $9^3/_4 + ^1/_2$ =

8. Is 15 a prime number?

9. 5　　　 15　　　 70 = 90

10. Write $^2/_{1\,000}$ as a decimal.

11. $^1/_2$ > 0.9

    ☐ *true* ☐ *false*

12. Simplify $^{30}/_{90}$.

13. Round 15.409 to 2 decimal places.

14. A tetrahedron has:

    faces　

    edges

    vertices

15. 33.9, 30.7, 27.5

    Rule =

16. 9.97, 9.98, 9.99,

17. 2 kg 79 g = $^{279}/_{1\,000}$ kg

    = 2.　　　 kg

18. 2 x a = 1 000

    so a =

19. Is 34 a multiple of 4?

20. The angles in a quadrilateral all add up to

    　　　 º.

21. If there are 8 000 Girltown Blues fans and 4 000 Bored Adelaide fans, what is the ratio?

22. What is the perimeter of a regular hexagon with 9-cm sides?

    　　　 cm

23. Draw an ellipse.

24. Which is the best value for money?

    ☐ *200 g of peas at €0.45*

    ☐ *500 g of peas at €1.00*

25. What is the probability of selecting a green jellybean from a jar if there are 50 green, 100 red and 100 white jellybeans?

    　　　 in

1. $^-4 + ^-5 =$

2. 20% of €60.00 =

   €

3. 800, 1 500, _____ , 2 900

4. 0.9 x 0.3 =

5. 5 m 2 cm = $5^2/_{100}$ m =

   5. _____ m

6. Draw and mark sides to show a kite.

7. Round 2.48 to the nearest tenth.

8. How many degrees make up a square?

9. 70 x a = 210 *so*

   a =

10. (3 ___ 8) ___ 6 = 30

11. What will I pay for a €90 jacket if there is a 50% reduction?

    €

12. Simplify the ratio.

    4:16 = 1:___ .

13. Round 15.937 to 2 decimal places.

14. Write $^2/_{1\,000}$ as a decimal.

15. What is the average of **6**, **8**, **16**, **10**?

16. Write in ascending order.

    0.22, 2, 2.2, 2.22

    _____ , _____ ,

    _____ , _____

17. Draw the axes of symmetry on the pentagon.

18. $^3/_5 + ^4/_5 + ^3/_5 =$

19.

    How many B boxes fit into Box A?

20. Which is the best value for money?

    ☐ *400 g sugar at €2.10*

    ☐ *500 g sugar at €2.50*

21. 16.2, 32.4, 64.8

    Rule =

22. Draw the net of a tetrahedron.

23. 7 x ___ = 2 x 14

24. 5.204 + 2.715 =

25. What speed is a car travelling at if it does 4 km every 5 minutes?

    _____ km/hr

1. 0.5 x 0.3 =

2. Add brackets to this number sentence.

   60 ÷ 10 x 1 + 9 − 6 = 54

3. 6 m 20 cm = $6^{20}/_{100}$ m

   = 6.____ m

4. a° =

5. Name this shape.

6. $^-8 + ^-3 =$

7. 0.02 = _____ %

8. 6 000 − a = 300 x 10

   so a =

9. 7.85, 7.90, 7.95, _____

10. $^6/_{20} + ^{19}/_{20} =$

11. 10 ___ (3 ___ 4) = 22

12. Parts of South America are 5 hours behind GMT. If it is 7 p.m. in London, what time is it in South America?

13. What will I pay for a €70 dress if there is a 50% discount?

    €

14. Simplify the ratio.

    4:24 = 1:___

15. If the radius of a circle is 60 cm, what is the diameter?

    _____ cm

16. Round 20.527 to 2 decimal places.

17. Simplify $^{16}/_{20}$.

18. $^9/_{10} − ^5/_{10} =$

19. If there are $0.90 (US) to €1.00, how many euro would you get for $18.00 (US)?

20. 3 kg 4 g = $3^4/_{1\,000}$ kg =

    3. _____ kg

21. 80, 40, 20, 10

    Rule =

22. 3.408 + 2.161 =

23. Is 25 a multiple of 3 and 5?

24. If a blue car is travelling at 80 km/hr, how far can the car travel in 1 hour?

    _____ km

25. What is the chance of selecting a green jelly sweet from a jar which has 20 yellow, 20 green and 60 red jellies?

    _____ in _____

FRIDAY TEST *Week 23*

1. $^-5 + ^-8 =$

2. $1 = \qquad \%$

3. Simplify $^{12}/_{15}$.

4. Double 28.5.

5. $5^1/_5 - ^3/_5 =$

6. Draw the net of a cone.

7. Is 24 a prime number?

8. $1.4 \times 0.3 =$

9. 75% of €200.00 =

    €

10. Double the size of this shape.

11. $(5 \qquad 7) \qquad 4 = 31$

12. $3.048 + 2.527 =$

13. Is 15 a multiple of 3 and 6?

14. Simplify the ratio.

    $7:35 = 1 :$

15. What is the perimeter of a regular hexagon with 50-mm sides?

    mm

16. Write in descending order.
    $^1/_5, ^1/_3, ^3/_{10}, ^1/_{100}$

    _____ , _____ ,

    _____ , _____

17. $y° =$

18. Round 4.477 to the nearest hundredth.

19. The time is 3.15 p.m. in Ireland and 8.15 p.m. in India. What is the time difference?

20. $(400 \div 40) \div 5 =$

21. A circular driveway has a 3 m radius. What is the diameter?

    m

22. Name this shape.

23. 77, 154, 308, _____

24. The shape in Question 22 has:

    faces _____

    edges _____

    vertices _____

25. If a car travels $4^1/_2$ km in 3 minutes, how far can it travel in 1 hour?

    km

FRIDAY TEST *Week 24*

1. $1.9 \times 0.2 =$

2. $^1/_4 = 0.$

3. $^-3 + ^-4 =$

4.

   Double this shape.

5. A television costs €400 plus 20% VAT. What is the total price?

   €

6. $10 - e = 9^1/_2$

   so e =

7. $7^2/_5 - ^4/_5 =$

8. $(2\,000 \div 20) \div 5 =$

9. $7^2 =$

10. $8.476 - 3.054 =$

11. 3 679 mL = _____

    litres

12. Are 18 and 19 both composite numbers?

13. Round 6.5038 to 3 decimal places.

14. $x =$

15. Double 15.5.

16. $7^3/_4 + 3^3/_4 =$

17. $(50 \qquad 2) \qquad 5 = 30$

18. $7^3/_7 =$
    (improper fraction).

19.

    Draw a 270° clockwise turn.

20. A triangular prism has:

    faces _____

    edges _____

    vertices _____

21. $4.295 + 2.334 =$

22. The angles in a rhombus add up to

    _____ °

23. 333 mL = $^1/_3$ L =

    0. _____ L

24. 75% = 0.7

    ☐ *true* ☐ *false*

25. What is the chance of choosing a red jellybean from a jar containing 1 red and 99 green ones? (No looking!)

    _____ in _____

1. Is 23 a prime number?

2. $^-9 + {}^-6 =$

3. $605 - y = 305$

   so y =

4. Halve $^1/_4$.

5. A computer costs €1 000 plus 20% VAT. What is the total price?

   €

6. 1.6 x 0.2=

7. Write in descending order.
   $^1/_2$, 0.55, 5%, 0.1

   ____ , ____ ,

   ____ ,

8. 7.249 − 3.085 =

9. Round 14.8569 to 3 decimal places.

10. 200 mL = $^1/_5$ L =

    0. ____ litres.

11. Write $^4/_{1\,000}$ as a decimal.

    0.

12. Are 200 and 255 both composite numbers?

13. (9 000 ÷ 30) ÷ 3 =

14. 40% = 0.04
    ☐ *true* ☐ *false*

15. The angles in a triangle are 35° and 110°. What is the third angle?

    °

16. Write $2^1/_4$ as a decimal.

17. a° =

18. Write $^5/_{1\,000}$ as a decimal.

19.

    Turn the rectangle 180° clockwise and draw the new position.

20. If $^2/_3$ of your class of 27 ate cereal in the morning, how many did not?

21. (8 ____ 5) ____ 15 = 25

22. The angles in a trapezium add up to

    °

23. 60% = 0.6
    ☐ *true* ☐ *false*

24. How many faces on a square pyramid?

25. Draw the net of a triangular prism.

    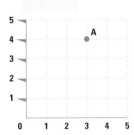

1. 0.97, 0.98, 0.99, ____

2. $^-3 + {}^-8 =$

3. $64 = 2^a$ so

   a =

4. 1.6 x 0.3 =

5. Write the co-ordinates of point A.

   ```
   5
   4            A
   3
   2
   1
   0   1   2   3   4   5
   ```

6. 9 x 6 =

7. $^{14}/_{20} = 0.$

8. The total cost of 6 pens is 66c what is the average cost of a pen?

   c

9. The meaning of 8 in 28 045 is

10. Can a triangle, square and circle tessellate together?

11. 2y + 2 = 20

    so y =

12. A car costs €20 000 plus 20% VAT. What is the total price?

    €

13. Two angles in a triangle are 95° and 50°. What is the 3rd angle?

    °

14. Draw the net of a cube.

15. 8.439 − 2.127 =

16. Tick the largest.
    ☐ *75% of 40*
    ☐ *35% of 100*

17. 40% of €500.00 =

    €

18. 750 mL = $^3/_4$ L =

    0. ____ L

19. Can an ellipse tessellate?

20. $9^6/_8 + 4^7/_8 =$

21. 25% = 0.25
    ☐ *true* ☐ *false*

22. If the radius of a circle is 10 cm, what is the diameter?

    cm

23. What is the chance of throwing an even number on a dice?

    in

24. How many right angles in an isosceles triangle?

25. If you are paid €4.50 per hour as a chocolate cake tester, what should you earn after 5 hours?

    €

1. How many right angles in a trapezium?

2. 450, 900, 1 350, _____ , 2 250

3. Halve 0.06.

4. 50 x 60 = a + 1 800

   so a =

5. 2% = 0.

6. ⁻3 + ⁺7 =

7. 6.3 − 0.8 =

8. 1.5 x 0.4 =

9. Round 4.2718 to 3 decimal places.

10. The value of 7 in 750 920 is

11. Write the co-ordinates of point A.

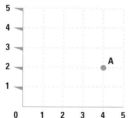

12. What is the floor area of a classroom 9 m by 7 m?

    m²

13. ⁷/₂₀ = 0.

14. 40 _____ (8 _____ 4) = 8

15. Name this triangle.

16. A car costs €1 500 plus 20% VAT. What is the total price?

    €

17. Two angles in a triangle are 65° and 65°. What is the third angle?

    °

18. 800 g = 0. _____ kg

19. What should the size of each angle in this rectangle be?

    °

20. Write three million, thirty-three thousand, five hundred as a numeral.

21. 6 pencils cost 90c. What is the average cost of a pencil?

    c

22.

    Draw to show a 90° turn anticlockwise.

23. Your chocolate cake testing job pays time and a half on Saturday. If you work for 2 hours, what should you earn if the normal rate is €5.00 an hour?

    €

24. If there are £0.60 (UK) to €1.00, how many euro would you get for £6.00 (UK)?

25. 750 mL = ³/₄ L =

    0. _____ litres

1. Which pyramid has 6 faces?

2. ⁻3 + ⁺7 =

3. Write three capital letters which are symmetrical.

4. Write the co-ordinates of point A.

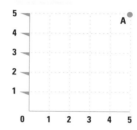

5. 1.7 x 0.2 =

6. Round 0.067 to the nearest hundredth.

7. 25 mL = 0. _____ L

8. Sam is travelling at 60 km per hour. How long will it take to travel 6 km?

    _____ mins.

9. The place value of 5 in 50 270 is

10. 8.5% = 0.

11. (7 _____ 5) _____ 10 = 25

12. The area of the house is 300 m². What is the area of the garden?

    m²

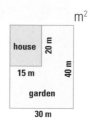

house 20 m
15 m   40 m
garden
30 m

13. The perimeter of the house is 70 m. What is the perimeter of the garden?

    m

14. Show as a 270° turn clockwise.

15. 3¹/₂ = _____ %

16. The angles in a triangle are 80° and 45°. What is the 3rd angle?

    °

17. 9 000, 18 000, 27 000, _____

18. 14 cm = _____ m

19. What is the average of these three cricket scores? **30, 15, 0**

20. How many edges has a cube?

21. 40% discount on a €200.00 item. How much do you save?

    €

22. If there are £0.60 (UK) to €1.00, how many euro would you get for £6.00 (UK)?

23. 7y + 7 = 28

    so y =

24. If you ride 7 km in a quarter of an hour, how far can you ride in 2 hours?

    km

25. 50% = ¹/₂ = 0.

1. $^-4 + {}^+9 =$

2. 268 kg = 0._____ t

3. Marie earns €500. She gets a 5% pay rise. What will her new wage be?

   €

4. 5 mm = 0._____ m

5. What do we call an angle that is between 90° and 180°?

6. John is travelling at 30 km per hour. How long will it take him to travel 20 km?

   _____ mins.

7. 250 mL = $\frac{1}{4}$ L =

   0._____ litres

8. 70% = $\frac{7}{10}$ = 0._____

9. 0.25, 0.5, 0.75, _____

10. $y° =$ _____°

y°
80°   35°

11. The place value of 7 in 1 769 302 is _____.

12. $6\frac{1}{2} \neq 6.2$

    ☐ true ☐ false

13. What number is halfway between −5 and +7?

14. 75 = y × 3

    so y =

15. Name this shape.

16. The total of 4 chocolate bars is 96c. What is the average cost of a chocolate bar?

    _____ c

17. Write in descending order.
    2.34, 18%, 0.11, 90%

    _____ , _____ ,

    _____ ,

18. How many edges on a hemisphere?

19. $\frac{1}{2} > \frac{4}{20}$

    ☐ true ☐ false

20. Round 20.4879 to three decimal places.

21. What is the area of a table 2.4 m by 0.5 m?

    _____ m²

22. A CD player costs €200 plus 20% VAT. What is the total price?

    €

23. What is the next square number after 49?

24. Which prism has 7 faces?

25. A strawberry jam factory loses $\frac{1}{10}$ of its jam to hungry workers. If they produce 1 000 L per week, how much do they lose each week?

    _____ L

1. 0.75 ÷ 0.25 =

2. Double 0.85.

3. $^-3 + {}^+9 =$

4. Rebecca earns €600. She has a 3% pay rise. What is her new wage?

   €

5. What number is halfway between −4 and +8?

6. How many edges on a cone?

7. How many faces on an octahedron?

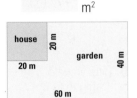

8. Which digit in the decimal 5.268 is the hundredth?

9. $\frac{1}{3}$ of y = 10

   so y =

10. 2.2% = 0._____

11. Halve $8\frac{1}{2}$.

12. What do we call an angle that is 90°?

13. $8\frac{6}{20} - \frac{10}{20} =$

14.

   110°
   x°

   x° = _____°

15. The total cost of 8 sweets is €1.34. What is the average cost of a sweet?

    _____ c

16. 9 700 m = _____ km

17. 140 mm = _____ m

18. What is the perimeter of a regular pentagon with 90 mm sides?

    _____ mm

19. Round 6.043 (nearest tenth).

20. A fridge costs €800 plus 20% VAT. What is the total price?

    €

21. The area of the house is 400 m². What is the area of the garden?

    _____ m²

    house 20 m
           20 m
    garden 40 m
    60 m

22. The perimeter of the house is 80 m. What is the perimeter of the garden?

    _____ m

23. 6.3, 6.9, 7.5, _____

24. If there are £0.60 (UK) to €1.00, how many euro would you get for £6.00 (UK)?

25. Write the co-ordinates of point A.

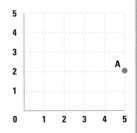

1. $0.8 \div 0.2 =$

2. $^-6 + {}^+9 =$

3. The total cost of 5 pizzas is €25.50. What is the average cost of a pizza?

   €

4. $^1/_{10} > ^1/_3$
   ☐ *true* ☐ *false*

5. $4 \text{ L } 295 \text{ mL} = 4^{295}/_{10\,000}$ L

   $= 4.$ _____ litres

6. Which digit in the decimal 5.052 is the tenth?

7. $0.1 =$ _____ %

8. 60 000, 150 000, 240 000, 330 000, _____

9. $60\% = {}^6/_{10} = 0.$ _____

10. What is the perimeter of a regular pentagon with 45-mm sides?

    _____ mm

11. Write a number that is symmetrical.

12.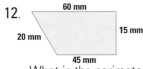
    What is the perimeter of this quadrilateral?

    _____ mm

13. Is the formulae area = L x W correct?

14. A cube has 2-cm by 2-cm faces. What is the cube's surface area?

    _____ cm³

15. Tick which would be the best to measure the length of a worm.
    ☐ *ruler*
    ☐ *trundle wheel*
    ☐ *metre stick*

16. An octahedron has

    faces _____

    edges _____

    vertices _____

17. What do we call an angle that is between 180° and 360°?

18. The place value of 5 in 450 277 is

19.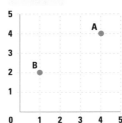
    Rotate this shape 450° anticlockwise and draw its new position.

20. Will a trapezium tessellate?

21. Write the co-ordinates of point A.

22. Write the co-ordinates of point B.

23. Round 6.464 (nearest tenth).

24. How many degrees make up a square?

    _____ °

25. Are 150 and 15 both composite numbers?

1. The place value of 4 in 4 378 200 is

2. Simplify $^{10}/_{12}$.

3. $10^2 - 3^2 =$

4. $y° =$

5. Rotate 450° clockwise.

   A

6. What do we call the angle that is between 180° and 360°?

7. 6 000, 12 000, 24 000, 48 000, _____

8. $(y + 50) = (80 + 90)$

   so y =

9. $1.6 \div 0.4 =$

10. $3^1/_3 + 3^2/_3 =$

11. Round 25.0917 to 3 decimal places.

12. Write the formulae to work out area.

    a = _____ x _____

13. Tick which scales would be best to weigh a child.
    ☐ *kitchen*
    ☐ *bathroom*

14. The total cost of 9 cakes is €3.15. What is the average cost of a cake?

    _____ c

15. $9^2 =$

16. $^-3 + {}^+7 =$

17. $6 \times y = 360$

    so y = _____

18. 2 075 mm = _____ m

19. ⊢———⊣
    Enlarge this line by 4:1.

    _____ mm

20. If there are ¥116 to €1.00, how many euro would you get for ¥580?

21. What is the area of a rectangular field 100 m by 15 m?

    _____ m²

22. $5 \text{ L } 25 \text{ mL} = {}^{525}/_{1\,000}$ L =

    5. _____ litres

23. Which digit in the decimal 2.347 is the hundredth?

24. What speed would you be travelling on your bike if it was doing $7^1/_2$ km every 30 minutes?

    _____ km/hr

25. A shape has six 2-cm by 5-cm faces. What is the shape's surface area?

    _____ cm³

1. $^3/_5$ of an hour = _____ minutes

2. $2.8 \div 0.7 =$

3. Write 3.2 million as a numeral.

4. Is the formulae: diameter = d x r correct?

5. Tick which scales would be best to weigh sweets.
   ☐ *kitchen*
   ☐ *bathroom*

6. 7 L 25 mL = $7^{25}/_{1\,000}$ L = 7. _____ litres

7. $^1/_4 \times ^1/_2 =$

8. The chance of me running at playtime is
   ☐ *0%*   ☐ *50%*
   ☐ *100%*

9. Draw a dot on co-ordinate (3,4) and label it 'A'.

10. Write in ascending order.
    3%, 0.3, $8^1/_2$, 51%
    _____ , _____ , _____ ,

11. A shape has six 1-cm by 7-cm faces. What is the shape's surface area?
    _____ cm³

12. Write the numeral twenty point three six.

13. 2.03 m = _____ cm

14. There are 0.6 euro to 1 Canadian dollar. How many euro would you exchange for 10 Canadian dollars?

15. 8.75 + 0.25 =

16. An octahedron has:
    faces
    edges
    vertices

17. Tick which would be the best to measure the length of a computer screen.
    ☐ *ruler*
    ☐ *trundle wheel*
    ☐ *metre stick*

18. $3^2 + 5^2 =$

19. ▬▬▬▬
    Enlarge this line by 3:1.
    _____ mm

20. (8 000 ÷ 80) x 50 =

21. **K** ▷
    Draw to show a rotation of 540° clockwise.

22. Round 16.5093 to 3 decimal places.

23. The chance of you talking during the next hour is
    ☐ *0%*   ☐ *50%*
    ☐ *100%*

24. Order the fractions from smallest to largest. $^1/_2$, $^8/_9$, $^1/_3$, $^4/_6$
    _____ , _____ ,
    _____ ,

25. $^-3 + {}^+6 =$

1. Write 4.73 million as a numeral.

2. $4.5 \div 0.5 =$

3. y x 200 = 1 000
   so y =

4. ▬▬▬▬▬
   Reduce line by 3:1.
   _____ mm

5. What volume of concrete is needed to fill a hole 8 m by 3 m by 2 m?
   _____ m³

6. Complete the formulae
   diameter = _____ x _____

7. 9.85, 9.9, 9.95, _____

8. 5 L 2 mL = $5^2/_{1\,000}$ L = 5. _____ litres

9. $^1/_5 \times ^1/_2 =$

10. What is the place value of 4 in 2.624?

11. The chance that it will rain today is
    ☐ *0%*   ☐ *50%*
    ☐ *100%*

12. $11^2 =$

13. A shape has eight 3-cm by 4-cm faces. What is the shape's surface area?
    _____ cm³

14. y° =

15. There are 6 euro to 10 Australian dollars. How many euro would you exchange for 30 Australian dollars?

16. What is the average of 60, 90, 30?

17. $^3/_4 + ^3/_4 + ^3/_4 =$

18. Tick which would be best to measure the capacity of a can of pop.
    ☐ *5 000 mL container*
    ☐ *1 000 mL jug*
    ☐ *100 mL beaker*

19.
    Show as a 270° turn clockwise.

20. $^1/_3 =$ _____ $/_6 =$ _____ $/_9$
    = _____ $/_{12}$

21. Round 21.5986 to 3 decimal places.

22. 200 seconds = _____ min _____ sec

23. The angles in a trapezium add up to _____ °

24. What is the area of this sail?
    _____ m²
    10 m
    10 m

25. Draw a dot on co-ordinate (4,0) and label it 'A'.

1. Tick which would be best to measure the capacity of a perfume bottle.
   ☐ *5 000 mL container*
   ☐ *1 000 mL jug*
   ☐ *100 mL beaker*

2. $\frac{4}{5} \times \frac{1}{2} =$

3. 2.36 kg =   g

4. 12.2, 12.4, 12.6, 12.8,

5. $\frac{4}{10} =$ %

6. ┣━━━━━━━━┫
   Reduce this line by 3:1.

            mm

7. Two coins are tossed in the air. The outcomes of how they land are:

   head and

   head and

   tail and

8. $\frac{1}{2} < 0.4999$
   ☐ *true* ☐ *false*

9. 6.4 ÷ 0.8 =

10. Parts of South America are 4 hours behind GMT. If it is 4.30 a.m. in London, what time is it in South America?

11. Complete the formulae:

    area =   x

12. The chance of rolling an even number on a dice is:
    ☐ *0%* ☐ *50%*
    ☐ *100%*

13. A shape has eight 2-cm by 5-cm faces. What is the shape's surface area?

         cm³

14. 25% of 160 =

15. 400 + 90 000 + 50 =

16. Is 400, 37 or 905 prime?

17.

    Double this shape.

18. 2 L 349 mL = $2^{349}/_{1\ 000}$ L

    = 2.   litres

19.
    (F)

    Show a rotation of 450° clockwise.

20. 9² =

21. Round 5.232 (nearest tenth).

22. If you are cycling at 24 km/hr, how far will you ride in 10 minutes?

         km

23. If your normal rate of pay is €7.00 per hour, what do you earn for 3 hours at time and a half?

    €

24. How many thirds in 4?

25. 2.3 − 0.7 =

1. The time is 9.20 a.m. in Ireland and 10.20 a.m. in France. What is the time difference?

2. Simplify $^{50}/_{100}$.

3. 5.6 ÷ 0.8 =

4. $\frac{1}{4} \times \frac{4}{5} =$

5. The chance that if you drop a piece of toast it will land buttered-side up is
   ☐ *0%* ☐ *50%*
   ☐ *100%*

6. A shape has ten 5-cm by 1-cm faces. What is the shape's surface area?

        cm³

7. 2 070 mm =

        m

8. Which would you use to measure the length of a pen?
   ☐ *mm* ☐ *cm*
   ☐ *m* ☐ *km*

9. ⁺4 − ⁺2 =

10. 5, $5^1/_4$, $5^3/_4$, $6^1/_2$,

11. 4 x   = 2 x 6

12. 8.3 + 0.7 =

13. What is the perimeter of a hexagon with 10-cm sides?

         cm

14. Tick which would be best to measure the capacity of a washing-up bowl.
    ☐ *5 000 mL container*
    ☐ *1 000 mL jug*
    ☐ *100 mL beaker*

15. There are 0.6 euro to 1 Canadian dollar. How many euro would you exchange for 20 Canadian dollars?

16. Draw the net of a cylinder

17. Complete the formulae:

    diameter =   x

18. Write in descending order. 0.32, 15%, 2.1

         ,   ,

19. 7 L 3 mL = $7^3/_{1\ 000}$ L

    = 7.   litres

20. If you were cycling at 36 km/hr, how far would you travel in 10 minutes?

         km

21. Which would you use to measure the weight of an apple?
    ☐ *g* ☐ *kg* ☐ *t*

22. Round 0.477 (nearest tenth).

23. What is the ratio of boys to girls if there are 80 girls and 40 boys?

24. What is the area of this sail?

    m²

25. 20 + 100 000 + 500 + 7 000 =

1. Double 4.07.

2. Which would you use to measure the amount of tea in a mug?
   ☐ mL   ☐ L

3. 2.4 ÷ 0.5 =

4. A shape has ten 2-cm by 3-cm faces. What is the shape's surface area?
   cm³

5. 90 000 + 3 + 600 =

6. What is the ratio of teachers to students if there are 10 teachers and 320 students?

7. 0, 1, 1, 2, 3, 5, 8,

8. What would you use to measure the length of a book?
   ☐ mm   ☐ cm
   ☐ m   ☐ km

9. Complete the formulae.
   diameter =   x

10. Which numeral is the tenth in 63.045?

11. $3^2/_{10}$ =   %

12.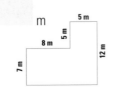
    Draw a 90° turn clockwise.

13. ⊢━━⊣
    Enlarge line by 5:1.
    mm

14. The chance of you growing taller in the next 5 years is
    ☐ 0%   ☐ 50%
    ☐ 100%

15. $^4/_{10}$ x $^1/_2$ =

16. There are 6 euro to 10 Australian dollars. How many euro would you exchange for 20 Australian dollars?

17. Which is longer?
    (a) *0.3 m* (b) *1 200 mm*
    (c) *40 cm*

18. Which would you use to measure the weight of a leaf?
    ☐ g   ☐ kg   ☐ t

19. Write $^{21}/_6$ as a mixed number.

20. Write 7.05 million as a numeral.

21. Tick the largest.
    ☐ $^5/_{10}$ ☐ $^6/_9$ ☐ $^2/_6$

22. Can an oval and a square tessellate together?

23. What is the average of the following shoe sizes?
    12, 8, 9, 11

24. Area =   m²
25. Perimeter =
    m

1. (900 ÷ 25) ÷ 4 =

2. 80 mm =
   cm

3. How many vertices on a cylinder?

4. 3, 8, 13, 18,

5. 2.7 ÷ 0.3 =

6. 4.06 + 0.67 =

7. What is the place value of 4 in 2.46 million?

8. Which would you use to measure the weight of a plane?
   ☐ g   ☐ kg   ☐ t

9. There are 6 euro to 10 Australian dollars. How many euro would you exchange for 30 Australian dollars?

10. y° =

    60°   y°

11. Write $5^3/_6$ as an improper fraction.

12. Which would you use to measure the amount of soup on a spoon?
    ☐ mL   ☐ L

13. What would you use to measure the thickness of a magazine?
    ☐ mm   ☐ cm
    ☐ m   ☐ km

14. 6.1 + 0.9 =

15. The LCD for $^1/_5$ and $^1/_4$ is   .

16. What is the perimeter of this regular pentagon?
    40 mm
    mm

17. $^3/_4$ x $^1/_3$ =

18. Name this shape.

19. Complete the formulae:
    area =

20. 49 is a multiple of 7.
    ☐ *true* ☐ *false*

21. A tank holds 1 000 L. If it is 85% full, how many litres is it holding?
    L

22. If a whiteboard is 1.5 m long and 1 m wide, what is the area?
    m²

23. The angles in a square are all
    °

24. How many hundreds in one million?

25. Draw a dot on coordinates (1,1), (1,3), (2,5), (3,3) and (3,1). Join them in order. What shape have you drawn?
    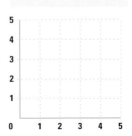

1. $7.7 \div 1.1 =$

2. $7^2 =$

3. How many faces on an octagonal prism?

4. Round 16.5087 to 3 decimal places.

5. Which has more faces, a triangular prism or a tetrahedron?

6. Which would you use to measure the amount of coffee in a mug?
   ☐ mL   ☐ L

7. How many edges on a hemisphere?

8. $5^1/_4$ km =

   _____ m

9. Which would you use to measure the width of your classroom?
   ☐ mm   ☐ cm
   ☐ m   ☐ km

10. 250 g = $^1/_4$ kg =

    0. _____ kg

11. $^9/_{10}$ = _____ %

12. $^1/_3 + ^2/_6 =$

13. 5.5 > 5.097
    ☐ true ☐ false

14. Sally scored $^8/_{10}$ in a maths test. Write this as a percentage.

    _____ %

15. Which would you use to measure the weight of 10 marbles?
    ☐ g ☐ kg ☐ t

16. $0.5 \times 0.3 =$

17. $60 + 400 + 5 =$

18. $^8/_9 - ^3/_9 =$

19. $40 - (5 \times 6) =$

20. Circle the largest.
    75% of 32   25% of 100

21. Write in descending order.
    300, 251, $^{500}/_1$

    _____ , _____ , _____

22. If you are cycling at 32 km/hr, how far can you travel in 15 minutes?

    _____ km

23. Write $^{15}/_4$ as a mixed number.

24. How many tenths in 1?

25. Write the missing angle.

    _____ °

1. Parts of the USA are 6 hours behind GMT. If it is 2.30 p.m. in London, what time is it in the USA?

2. $24 \div 0.2 =$

3. $^6/_{10} \times ^1/_2 =$

4. A car costs €20 000 plus 20% VAT. What is the total price?

   € _____

5. How many degrees in a triangle?

   _____ °

6. $3^6/_{10} =$
   (decimal)

7. Rotate 450° clockwise.

   Ⓐ

8. 20 _____ (10 _____ 8)
   = 10

9. $3.05 > 3^1/_{10}$
   ☐ true ☐ false

10. Which would you use to measure the length of a bus?
    ☐ mm   ☐ cm
    ☐ m   ☐ km

11. $0.8 \times 0.4 =$

12. $^-7 - ^+2 =$

13. Simplify the ratio.

    28:7 = _____ :1

14. Is 40 a multiple of 10 and 3?

15. A shape has eight 2-cm by 2-cm faces. What is the shape's surface area?

    _____ cm³

16. What will I pay for a €90.00 coat if there is a 60% discount?

    € _____

17. 1, 2, 4, 7, 11, _____

18. $5 \times y = 60$

    so y = _____

19. 1 m + 50 cm =

    _____ cm

20. $(500 \div 25) \div 5 =$

21. $11^2 =$

22. $^-6 + ^+12 =$

23. Write 3.9 million as a numeral.

24. The angles in a triangle are 65° and 90°. What is the 3rd angle?

    _____ °

25. Draw the net of a pentagonal prism.

Place value

9 741.258	thousands	hundreds	tens	units	•	tenths	hundredths	thousandths

9 741.258
9 000.000
  700.000
   40.000
    1.000
     .200
     .050
     .008

thousands	hundreds	tens	units	•	tenths	hundredths	thousandths
9	7	4	1	•	2	5	8

Prime numbers

A prime number is a number that can be divided evenly by only 1 and itself.

For example: 2, 3, 5, 7 and 11.

Composite numbers

A composite number is a number that can be divided by more than 1 and itself, i.e. it has more than 2 divisors.

For example: 4, 6, 8, 9 and 10.

Factors

A factor of a number is a number that will divide evenly into that number.

For example:
The factors of 12 are 1, 2, 3, 4, 6 and 12.

Multiples

A multiple of a number is a number multiplied by other whole numbers.

For example:
The multiples of 5 are 5, 10, 15, 20, 25, 30 …

Square and rectangular numbers

A square number is a number that can form the shape of a square.

For example: 4, 9, 16, 25 …

9

A rectangular number is a number that can form the shape of a rectangle.

For example: 6, 8, 10, 12 …

6

Odd and even numbers

Odd numbers end in 1, 3, 5, 7 or 9.
For example: 95, 317, 821, 9 999

Even numbers end in 0, 2, 4, 6 or 8.
For example: 54, 720, 1 636, 9 998

Multiplication and division facts

Multiplication and division facts are linked together. If you know one multiplication fact you also have the ability to know three other related facts.

For example:
If you know the fact $4 \times 5 = 20$
You will also know the facts $5 \times 4 = 20$ and $20 \div 4 = 5$ and $20 \div 5 = 4$

2x

table	other facts I know		
1 x 2 = 2	2 x 1 = 2	2 ÷ 2 = 1	2 ÷ 1 = 2
2 x 2 = 4		4 ÷ 2 = 2	
3 x 2 = 6	2 x 3 = 6	6 ÷ 2 = 3	6 ÷ 3 = 2
4 x 2 = 8	2 x 4 = 8	8 ÷ 2 = 4	8 ÷ 4 = 2
5 x 2 = 10	2 x 5 = 10	10 ÷ 2 = 5	10 ÷ 5 = 2
6 x 2 = 12	2 x 6 = 12	12 ÷ 2 = 6	12 ÷ 6 = 2
7 x 2 = 14	2 x 7 = 14	14 ÷ 2 = 7	14 ÷ 7 = 2
8 x 2 = 16	2 x 8 = 16	16 ÷ 2 = 8	16 ÷ 8 = 2
9 x 2 = 18	2 x 9 = 18	18 ÷ 2 = 9	18 ÷ 9 = 2
10 x 2 = 20	2 x 10 = 20	20 ÷ 2 = 10	20 ÷ 10 = 2

3x

table	other facts I know		
1 x 3 = 3	3 x 1 = 3	3 ÷ 3 = 1	3 ÷ 1 = 3
2 x 3 = 6	3 x 2 = 6	6 ÷ 3 = 2	6 ÷ 2 = 3
3 x 3 = 9		9 ÷ 3 = 3	
4 x 3 = 12	3 x 4 = 12	12 ÷ 3 = 4	12 ÷ 4 = 3
5 x 3 = 15	3 x 5 = 15	15 ÷ 3 = 5	15 ÷ 5 = 3
6 x 3 = 18	3 x 6 = 18	18 ÷ 3 = 6	18 ÷ 6 = 3
7 x 3 = 21	3 x 7 = 21	21 ÷ 3 = 7	21 ÷ 7 = 3
8 x 3 = 24	3 x 8 = 24	24 ÷ 3 = 8	24 ÷ 8 = 3
9 x 3 = 27	3 x 9 = 27	27 ÷ 3 = 9	27 ÷ 9 = 3
10 x 3 = 30	3 x 10 = 30	30 ÷ 3 = 10	30 ÷ 10 = 3

4x

table	other facts I know		
1 x 4 = 4	4 x 1 = 4	4 ÷ 4 = 1	4 ÷ 1 = 4
2 x 4 = 8	4 x 2 = 8	8 ÷ 4 = 2	8 ÷ 2 = 4
3 x 4 = 12	4 x 3 = 12	12 ÷ 4 = 3	12 ÷ 3 = 4
4 x 4 = 16		16 ÷ 4 = 4	
5 x 4 = 20	4 x 5 = 20	20 ÷ 4 = 5	20 ÷ 5 = 4
6 x 4 = 24	4 x 6 = 24	24 ÷ 4 = 6	24 ÷ 6 = 4
7 x 4 = 28	4 x 7 = 28	28 ÷ 4 = 7	28 ÷ 7 = 4
8 x 4 = 32	4 x 8 = 32	32 ÷ 4 = 8	32 ÷ 8 = 4
9 x 4 = 36	4 x 9 = 36	36 ÷ 4 = 9	36 ÷ 9 = 4
10 x 4 = 40	4 x 10 = 40	40 ÷ 4 = 10	40 ÷ 10 = 4

5x

table	other facts I know		
1 x 5 = 5	5 x 1 = 5	5 ÷ 5 = 1	5 ÷ 1 = 5
2 x 5 = 10	5 x 2 = 10	10 ÷ 5 = 2	10 ÷ 2 = 5
3 x 5 = 15	5 x 3 = 15	15 ÷ 5 = 3	15 ÷ 3 = 5
4 x 5 = 20	5 x 4 = 20	20 ÷ 5 = 4	20 ÷ 4 = 5
5 x 5 = 25		25 ÷ 5 = 5	
6 x 5 = 30	5 x 6 = 30	30 ÷ 5 = 6	30 ÷ 6 = 5
7 x 5 = 35	5 x 7 = 35	35 ÷ 5 = 7	35 ÷ 7 = 5
8 x 5 = 40	5 x 8 = 40	40 ÷ 5 = 8	40 ÷ 8 = 5
9 x 5 = 45	5 x 9 = 45	45 ÷ 5 = 9	45 ÷ 9 = 5
10 x 5 = 50	5 x 10 = 50	50 ÷ 5 = 10	50 ÷ 10 = 5

6x

table	other facts I know		
1 x 6 = 6	6 x 1 = 6	6 ÷ 6 = 1	6 ÷ 1 = 6
2 x 6 = 12	6 x 2 = 12	12 ÷ 6 = 2	12 ÷ 2 = 6
3 x 6 = 18	6 x 3 = 18	18 ÷ 6 = 3	18 ÷ 3 = 6
4 x 6 = 24	6 x 4 = 24	24 ÷ 6 = 4	24 ÷ 4 = 6
5 x 6 = 30	6 x 5 = 30	30 ÷ 6 = 5	30 ÷ 5 = 6
6 x 6 = 36		36 ÷ 6 = 6	
7 x 6 = 42	6 x 7 = 42	42 ÷ 6 = 7	42 ÷ 7 = 6
8 x 6 = 48	6 x 8 = 48	48 ÷ 6 = 8	48 ÷ 8 = 6
9 x 6 = 54	6 x 9 = 54	54 ÷ 6 = 9	54 ÷ 9 = 6
10 x 6 = 60	6 x 10 = 60	60 ÷ 6 = 10	60 ÷ 10 = 6

7x

table	other facts I know		
1 x 7 = 7	7 x 1 = 7	7 ÷ 7 = 1	7 ÷ 1 = 7
2 x 7 = 14	7 x 2 = 14	14 ÷ 7 = 2	14 ÷ 2 = 7
3 x 7 = 21	7 x 3 = 21	21 ÷ 7 = 3	21 ÷ 3 = 7
4 x 7 = 28	7 x 4 = 28	28 ÷ 7 = 4	28 ÷ 4 = 7
5 x 7 = 35	7 x 5 = 35	35 ÷ 7 = 5	35 ÷ 5 = 7
6 x 7 = 42	7 x 6 = 42	42 ÷ 7 = 6	42 ÷ 6 = 7
7 x 7 = 49		49 ÷ 7 = 7	
8 x 7 = 56	7 x 8 = 56	56 ÷ 7 = 8	56 ÷ 8 = 7
9 x 7 = 63	7 x 9 = 63	63 ÷ 7 = 9	63 ÷ 9 = 7
10 x 7 = 70	7 x 10 = 70	70 ÷ 7 = 10	70 ÷ 10 = 7

8x

table	other facts I know		
1 x 8 = 8	8 x 1 = 8	8 ÷ 8 = 1	8 ÷ 1 = 8
2 x 8 = 16	8 x 2 = 16	16 ÷ 8 = 2	16 ÷ 2 = 8
3 x 8 = 24	8 x 3 = 24	24 ÷ 8 = 3	24 ÷ 3 = 8
4 x 8 = 32	8 x 4 = 32	32 ÷ 8 = 4	32 ÷ 4 = 8
5 x 8 = 40	8 x 5 = 40	40 ÷ 8 = 5	40 ÷ 5 = 8
6 x 8 = 48	8 x 6 = 48	48 ÷ 8 = 6	48 ÷ 6 = 8
7 x 8 = 56	8 x 7 = 56	56 ÷ 8 = 7	56 ÷ 7 = 8
8 x 8 = 64		64 ÷ 8 = 8	
9 x 8 = 72	8 x 9 = 72	72 ÷ 8 = 9	72 ÷ 9 = 8
10 x 8 = 80	8 x 10 = 80	80 ÷ 8 = 10	80 ÷ 10 = 8

9x

table	other facts I know		
1 x 9 = 9	9 x 1 = 9	9 ÷ 9 = 1	9 ÷ 1 = 9
2 x 9 = 18	9 x 2 = 18	18 ÷ 9 = 2	18 ÷ 2 = 9
3 x 9 = 27	9 x 3 = 27	27 ÷ 9 = 3	27 ÷ 3 = 9
4 x 9 = 36	9 x 4 = 36	36 ÷ 9 = 4	36 ÷ 4 = 9
5 x 9 = 45	9 x 5 = 45	45 ÷ 9 = 5	45 ÷ 5 = 9
6 x 9 = 54	9 x 6 = 54	54 ÷ 9 = 6	54 ÷ 6 = 9
7 x 9 = 63	9 x 7 = 63	63 ÷ 9 = 7	63 ÷ 7 = 9
8 x 9 = 72	9 x 8 = 72	72 ÷ 9 = 8	72 ÷ 8 = 9
9 x 9 = 81		81 ÷ 9 = 9	
10 x 9 = 90	9 x 10 = 90	90 ÷ 9 = 10	90 ÷ 10 = 9

10x

table	other facts I know		
1 x 10 = 10	10 x 1 = 10	10 ÷ 10 = 1	10 ÷ 1 = 10
2 x 10 = 20	10 x 2 = 20	20 ÷ 10 = 2	20 ÷ 2 = 10
3 x 10 = 30	10 x 3 = 30	30 ÷ 10 = 3	30 ÷ 3 = 10
4 x 10 = 40	10 x 4 = 40	40 ÷ 10 = 4	40 ÷ 4 = 10
5 x 10 = 50	10 x 5 = 50	50 ÷ 10 = 5	50 ÷ 5 = 10
6 x 10 = 60	10 x 6 = 60	60 ÷ 10 = 6	60 ÷ 6 = 10
7 x 10 = 70	10 x 7 = 70	70 ÷ 10 = 7	70 ÷ 7 = 10
8 x 10 = 80	10 x 8 = 80	80 ÷ 10 = 8	80 ÷ 8 = 10
9 x 10 = 90	10 x 9 = 90	90 ÷ 10 = 9	90 ÷ 9 = 10
10 x 10 = 100		100 ÷ 10 = 10	

Fractions

Numerator
The number above the line, indicating how many parts are in consideration.

$$\frac{3}{4}$$

Denominator
The number below the line, indicating how many parts the whole number is divided into.

Equivalent fractions

one whole							
¹/₂				¹/₂			
¹/₄		¹/₄		¹/₄		¹/₄	
¹/₈	¹/₈	¹/₈	¹/₈	¹/₈	¹/₈	¹/₈	¹/₈

¹/₃		¹/₃		¹/₃	
¹/₆	¹/₆	¹/₆	¹/₆	¹/₆	¹/₆

¹/₉	¹/₉	¹/₉	¹/₉	¹/₉	¹/₉	¹/₉	¹/₉	¹/₉
¹/₁₂	¹/₁₂	¹/₁₂	¹/₁₂	¹/₁₂	¹/₁₂	¹/₁₂	¹/₁₂	¹/₁₂ ¹/₁₂ ¹/₁₂ ¹/₁₂

¹/₅		¹/₅		¹/₅		¹/₅		¹/₅	
¹/₁₀	¹/₁₀	¹/₁₀	¹/₁₀	¹/₁₀	¹/₁₀	¹/₁₀	¹/₁₀	¹/₁₀	¹/₁₀

Fractions, decimals and percentages

Fraction	Decimal	Percentage
¹/₂	0.5	50%
¹/₃	0.33	33%
¹/₄	0.25	25%
¹/₅	0.2	20%

Fraction	Decimal	Percentage
¹/₈	0.125	12.5%
¹/₁₀	0.1	10%
¹/₁₀₀	0.01	1%

The circle

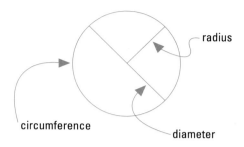

radius

circumference

diameter

Diameter: a line that divides a circle into half. The diameter is twice the length of the radius (d = 2 x r).

Radius: a line that joins the centre of a circle to a point on the edge.

Circumference: the distance around a circle (its perimeter).

2-D shapes – triangles

A triangle is a shape with 3 sides and 3 angles. The total of the angles adds up to 180°.

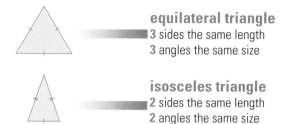

equilateral triangle
3 sides the same length
3 angles the same size

isosceles triangle
2 sides the same length
2 angles the same size

scalene triangle
0 sides the same length
0 angles the same size

2-D shapes – quadrilaterals

A quadrilateral is a shape with 4 sides and 4 angles. The total of the angles adds up to 360°.

square	**rectangle**	**rhombus**	**parallelogram**	**trapezium**
4 sides the same length	2 pairs of sides the same length	4 sides the same length	2 pairs of sides the same length	1 pair of sides the same length
4 angles the same size	4 angles the same size	2 pairs of angles the same size	2 pairs of angles the same size	1 pair of sides different length
				2 pairs of angles the same size

Other 2-D shapes

circle	**semicircle**	**oval**	**pentagon**	**hexagon**	**octagon**
1 side	**2** sides	**1** side	**5** sides	**6** sides	**8** sides
0 corners	**2** corners	**0** corners	**5** corners	**6** corners	**8** corners

3-D shapes

cube	**cuboid**	**cylinder**	**cone**	**sphere**	**triangular prism**
6 faces 12 edges	6 faces 12 edges	3 faces 2 edges	2 faces 1 edge	1 face 0 edges	5 faces 9 edges
8 vertices	8 vertices	0 vertices	1 vertice	0 vertices	6 vertices

pentagonal prism	**hexagonal prism**	**tetrahedron** (triangular-based pyramid)	**square-based pyramid**	**octahedron**
7 faces 15 edges	8 faces 18 edges	4 faces 6 edges	5 faces 8 edges	8 faces 12 edges
10 vertices	12 vertices	4 vertices	5 vertices	6 vertices

Nets of 3-D shapes

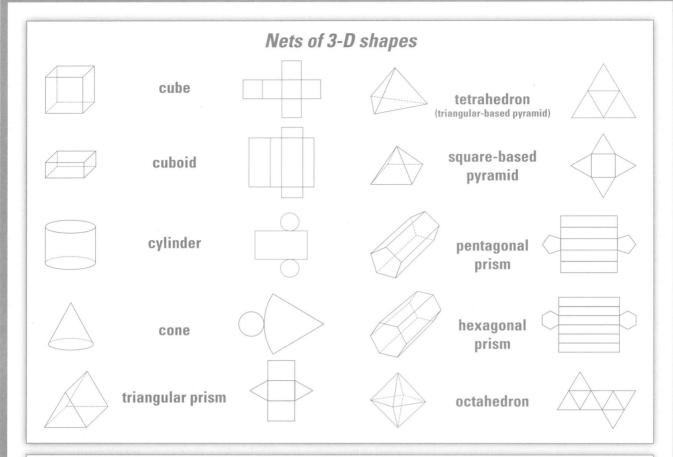

Lines

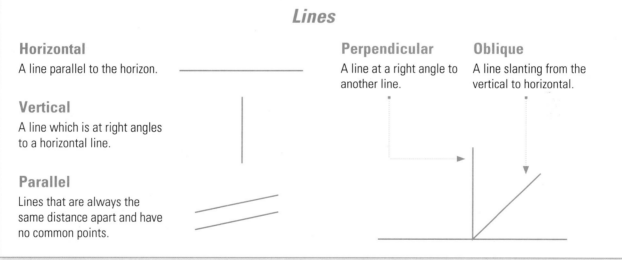

Horizontal
A line parallel to the horizon.

Vertical
A line which is at right angles to a horizontal line.

Parallel
Lines that are always the same distance apart and have no common points.

Perpendicular
A line at a right angle to another line.

Oblique
A line slanting from the vertical to horizontal.

Angles

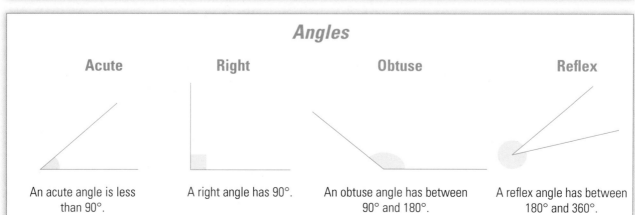

Acute
An acute angle is less than 90°.

Right
A right angle has 90°.

Obtuse
An obtuse angle has between 90° and 180°.

Reflex
A reflex angle has between 180° and 360°.